Schedule, Cost, and Profit Control with PERT

Schedule, Cost, and Profit Control with PERT

A Comprehensive Guide for Program Management

ROBERT W. MILLER

Vice President
Defense & Space Systems Management
United Research, Inc.
Washington, D.C.

McGRAW-HILL BOOK COMPANY, INC.

New York   San Francisco   Toronto

London   Sydney

To Marie-Jeanne, Philip, and Stephen

Preface

The reader may ask: "Why a book entitled *Schedule, Cost, and Profit Control with PERT?* Isn't PERT (Program Evaluation and Review Technique) the name of a scheduling system designed for government programs, which is fairly straightforward in concept, and which has been thoroughly documented?"

By 1963 it seemed important to answer questions such as these in a book written for both top management and operating people in both commercial and government-based industries. In addition, within the worlds of government and education, it seemed clear that the significance of PERT Management Systems, as they have evolved through the period of 1963, had not been fully recognized. Readers of this book will soon discover that it is indeed concerned with the problems of planning and control in the three dimensions of schedule, cost, and profits, and that the basic approach is founded upon the technique of networking.

The frame of reference in which PERT is best applied is quite different from the situation in which classical control methods are used. Thus the reader will find throughout the book an emphasis on the problems of *program management,* as distinguished from those of established *functional management.* Perhaps a quotation from Jay W. Forrester, in the introduction of his volume on *Industrial Dynamics,* sets the theme of my book as well as it can be stated: *

> Until now much of management education and practice has dealt only with components. Accounting, production, marketing, finance, human relations, and economics have been taught and practiced as if they were separate, unrelated subjects. Only in the topmost managerial positions do managers need to integrate the separate functions. Our industrial systems are becoming so large and complex that a knowledge of the parts taken separately is not sufficient. In management as in engineering, we can expect that the interconnections and interactions between the components of the system will often be more important than the separate components themselves.

In this book we are explicitly concerned with the planning and control problems associated with special-purpose or "one-time-through" programs, as opposed to continuous production operations. In addition, we are concerned with the application of PERT techniques to areas of time, cost, and product performance, representing an integrated management approach to all three of these factors in modern programs.

The potential applications for such an integrated management approach range from the introduction of a new product in the commercial world to the acquisition of a large weapons system or a disarmament program. In between these categories there are a host of other applications, both large and small, where the full spectrum of PERT techniques described in this book may not always be applicable. Basically, however, the book emphasizes those aspects of PERT techniques which are involved in the actual management and execution of special-purpose programs of any complexity. The role of PERT in the areas of long-range planning and of early conceptual or decision-making phases is discussed, but the emphasis is on actual implementation of programs by industry. Nevertheless, the neces-

---

* Reprinted from *Industrial Dynamics,* 1961, p. 6, by Jay W. Forrester, by permission of The M.I.T. Press, Massachusetts Institute of Technology, Cambridge, Mass. All rights reserved.

sity for a close tie-in between aggregate or initial planning and PERT analysis is emphasized, for without this tie-in it is difficult for early planning efforts to have any real validity.

The treatment of the book is essentially historical. In Chapter 1 the developments of the 1950s leading to the evolution of networking techniques such as PERT and CPM are discussed. In Chapter 2 the methodology of networking, with PERT/TIME as the basic framework, is treated in detail. It is my hope that this chapter will prove informative, not only for the executive who thinks of PERT as "just a scheduling system" (or perhaps has not even been exposed to its basic methodology), but also to the PERT analyst and persons working directly with the technique who have not kept up with the latest developments in the field of PERT/TIME. In Chapter 3 the pros and cons and problems of implementation are discussed, from the point of view of both top management and operating-level management. In Chapter 4 the specific features and problems of PERT/COST are treated in detail, with emphasis on the requirements of the Department of Defense PERT/COST system. In this chapter I have attempted to cover the problems of PERT/COST from the point of view of the financial executive or controller, as well as the program manager and functional manager.

Chapter 5 covers some of the latest developments in PERT Management Systems. In particular it emphasizes their relationship to the formalized requirements of Project Definition, systems engineering, value engineering, and Configuration Management. This chapter was written especially for the managers of the large, complex development programs of our time; however, many of its principles are applicable to smaller programs.

In Chapter 6, methods of organizing for the implementation of PERT Management Systems are discussed; here the roles of both program management and a central PERT staff are treated. In the discussion of PERT and its relationship to profits, I have emphasized both commercial and government business in terms of data on actual applications and payoffs. I hope this section of

Chapter 6 will be of interest to management in both fields. When it comes to the difficult subject of the relationship of PERT to *multiple-incentive contracting,* however, it must be recognized that we are dealing with the problems of large, complex military and space development programs, which are planned and executed in the demanding environment of our times. This section should be of particular interest to contract managers in both government and industry.

Much of the subject matter covered in this book may raise questions concerning the degree of government influence over the management process in the defense and space industries. There is no question but that an entirely new relationship has developed between government and industry in connection with the conduct of the large, complex programs previously referred to; in connection with PERT reporting requirements, the line which the government normally should not pass is discussed in Chapter 4. It is important to emphasize, however, that the advantages of the use of PERT Management Systems are mutual; when they are properly applied by the industrial contractor, they can produce benefits for him as well as for the government. In fact, in the area of incentive contracting treated in Chapter 6, one may conclude that new opportunities are available for the superior contractor to earn profits which are more in line with established free-enterprise levels. It is, of course, too early to tell whether the objectives of incentive contracting and these beneficial results for industry will actually be realized.

The approach of this book is essentially pragmatic, largely because the proper application of PERT to problems of schedule, cost, and profit control is intrinsically a pragmatic one. Thus the "pure" operations researcher will not find much to challenge him here, with the possible exception of the conceptual model for the multiple-incentive contracting situation given in Chapter 6. In addition, the researcher in the field of R & D management problems will not find any extensive discussion of such areas as motivation and quality of personnel, propensity for risk taking, and techniques of communication. Researchers in this field should take note, however, of the rapid developments described in this book, which have outrun research efforts as a matter of vital necessity.

Finally, one may comment briefly on the social significance of the management systems described in this book. The possibility of producing a valid summarization of 30,000 network activities in a "condensed network" for the top industrial or government manager, as described in the section on network condensation and integration in Chapter 3, may have social significance for some. Nevertheless it is clear that these management systems are only tools for the manager at all levels, and that they will not replace him or the quality of his judgment. Readers with a social or philosophical bent may be interested in the discussion of objective-oriented planning, such as required by PERT, which is treated in the early part of Chapter 5. It should be clear from this discussion that PERT techniques are also applicable to problems of economic development and planning.

It is easy to decry the demands posed by PERT techniques and the complexity of its networks. Yet PERT is only a vehicle or mechanism for representing the very real complexities of the demanding undertakings of our time, which has been called the "age of massive engineering."

I wish to express my appreciation to the many people in my own company, and throughout the country in both government and industry, who contributed to this book. It would be impossible to name them all. In particular, however, I would like to mention the members of my EIA (Electronics Industries Association) Committee on PERT Management Systems; Mr. Charles Greer, who originated the conceptual approach to the handling of the profit dimension in Chapter 6 as a result of some unpublished work at M.I.T.; Mrs. Esther MacLeod, who typed the manuscript through all its revisions in the trying circumstances of a corporate headquarters office. Finally, it seems appropriate to acknowledge the support of my family, who accepted with forbearance the many weekends and holidays consumed in the preparation of this book.

Robert W. Miller

Contents

List of Figures

1

The Modern Management System Problem

The Impact of PERT

Since its introduction in 1958, the use of the network technique as a new management tool has spread rapidly and with far-reaching impact. Whether under the name of PERT (Program Evaluation and Review Technique) or CPM (Critical Path Method), the same basic concept has been used for a wide range of planning and control problems. These are as diverse as the development of a multibillion-dollar weapons system, the construction of a superhighway or ship, the installation of a data-processing system in a bank, and the introduction of a new commercial product, including its advertising campaign. Such projects have the common characteristic of being special-purpose, or "one-time-through"; this is the type of application where PERT excels.

The original time-oriented characteristic of PERT was extended during the period 1961 to 1962 to include manpower and cost elements. As of 1963, the technique was further integrated with systems engineering, or the initial technical defi-

1

nition of a project. Thus, for the first time, the three program elements of product performance, cost, and schedule were combined in an explicit planning and control system. As a result of these developments, the concept of PERT and CPM as a scheduling technique has been extended into the broader area of an integrated set of "PERT Management Systems." As such, they have become an important determinant of profit structures and return, and have a particularly significant impact on profits under incentive-type contracting arrangements.

Significance of PERT

PERT is now viewed as a major step forward for the management of nonrepetitive or one-time-through programs. As to its potential application and importance within the national economy, it should be pointed out that in just two major categories of nonrepetitive work, namely, research and development and nonresidential construction (including highways), United States expenditures were in excess of $50 billion in 1962. Even though PERT-type systems may not be applicable in all areas of this expenditure, their potential role is obviously very great.

As an addition to knowledge, PERT represents an important contribution to the family of management sciences, or operations research techniques. In fact, if one views the network as a model of one-time-through or nonrepetitive programs, PERT represents one of the most widely used models in existence today. Unfortunately, the model has been misused just as often as it has been properly used. It will be one of the purposes of this book to emphasize the correct application of PERT, in order to obtain maximum benefit out of its new features.

PERT is one of the techniques of management science where it is possible, in the case of actual application, to achieve payoffs with relatively *uncertain* planning and control problems. The two features of PERT which bring about this advantage are the *judicious use of three-way estimates*, which represent a relatively simple approach to the prediction of time uncertainty, and *flexibility of updating*, which allows a quick reaction to the impact of events as they actually occur. As a matter of fact, prior to the advent of PERT, it was generally believed that explicit planning and scheduling of research and development work was difficult, if not impossible. For this reason, it was not widely practiced. Today it is generally recognized that such a criterion at best applies only to the "research" end of the research and development spectrum, which, by most estimates, constitutes less than 10 per cent of total national expenditures in this field.

Finally, it became apparent in the early applications of PERT that it forced a depth of planning—largely through the special characteristics of the technique itself—which had often been assumed by managers, but which had rarely been carried out in actual industrial practice. On nonrepetitive programs it also became clear that, when properly applied, it had some *predictive* attributes not found in most management systems for such programs.

These, then, are the manifold reasons which have brought PERT into such rapid development and national prominence. In Chapter 3, we shall discuss in more detail the pros and cons of PERT/TIME with particular reference to its cost and proper areas and methods of application. In Chapter 4, the extension of PERT/TIME to PERT/COST will be similarly considered.

Meanwhile, as a background to the development of PERT/TIME and PERT/COST, we shall consider prior management systems and how they failed to solve the problems of management for complex, nonrepetitive programs on a large modern scale.

Prior Cost Systems

Most readers are familiar with the fact that the foundations of scientific management were established during the early 1900s by Frederick W. Taylor and his followers. By observation and measurement, they firmly established the concept of direct labor standards and control of direct labor costs. This basic approach then evolved into such management-system applications as measured piecework in repetitive factory operations.

It is important to emphasize that the concept of measuring direct labor costs in relation to volume of goods produced provided the central framework for cost control systems up until the era of PERT/COST. The introduction of "standard cost" and "flexible budget" systems, along with "break-even analysis" during the 1920s, depended upon this basic concept.

As is well known, in these systems costs are segregated into the categories of "directly variable," "semivariable," or "fixed," with respect to volume of goods produced. In order for such cost control systems to be effective or at all valid, the "variable costs" must be based on data established by industrial engineering practices, i.e., data of the type evolved by Taylor. The fixed or overhead elements in such cost control systems are generally handled on a "budgeted" basis, i.e., annual levels of expenditure are determined, generally by functional or organizational units, and usually without any specific identification of the cost of individual tasks within the overhead structure. It is important to mention that, with the introduction of "work-measurement" techniques in the late 1940s, the principle of examining the cost of individual *overhead* tasks was established. However, the basic approach was quite similar to the methods used by Taylor in establishing direct cost measurement.

Given a pricing structure and a sales forecast of goods produced, these approaches to cost and profit control worked very well for the majority of American businesses through the period of World War II and into the early 1950s. The success of these systems was predicated on high-volume production of standardized products, or at least products with an established bill of materials and associated standard costs. As we shall see, these approaches did not work on the large, nonstandard programs—i.e., programs with a high engineering content, which came increasingly to the fore in the mid 1950s.

Prior Scheduling Systems

Another technique going back to the early era of scientific management, and one more closely related to the beginnings of PERT, was the scheduling system introduced by Henry L. Gantt, one of the most important contemporaries of Taylor.

Figure 1 shows a typical Gantt Chart for a machine shop.[1] *

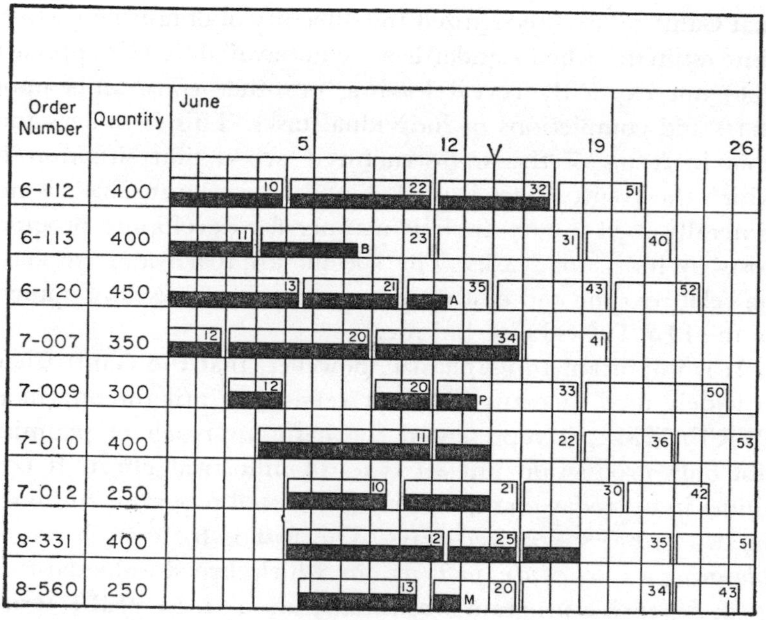

Order Number	Quantity	June 5	12	19	26
6-112	400	10	22	32	51
6-113	400	11 / B	23	31	40
6-120	450	13	21 / A	35 / 43	52
7-007	350	12	20	34	41
7-009	300	12	20 / P	33	50
7-010	400	11	22	36	53
7-012	250	10	21	30	42
8-331	400	12	25	35	51
8-560	250	13 / M	20	34	43

FIG. 1. Gantt progress chart.

Individual orders are described on the left-hand portion of the chart, and the scheduled times for accomplishing each order (shown by open bars) together with actual completion (shown by solid bars) are plotted along on a horizontal calendar scale. It is interesting to note that Gantt developed this approach in the context of a military requirement. During World War I

* Superscript numbers indicate items listed in the References at the end of the chapter.

he worked with the Army Bureau of Ordnance, and soon realized that a graphical method was required for portraying plans and status for the munitions program of that day. He also recognized that *time* was the one common denominator by which program plans, and progress or lack of progress against them, could be most quickly assessed. Gantt's approach also rests on the foundation of standard times, or relatively certain estimated times for setup and processing, although it is interesting to note that Gantt himself recognized the difficulty of obtaining realistic time estimates when standards were not available. His approach does not explicitly reveal loading or other constraints upon starts and completions of individual tasks. This is understandable in terms of the well-structured production situation in which the Gantt Chart is used. Finally, the Gantt Chart is not generally used in any explicit manner for developing program costs by individual tasks. The specific approach and emphasis on relating time and cost were to come out of the development of the PERT/COST technique.

It is important to emphasize, however, that the Gantt Chart is widely used in many different versions. Until the advent of PERT/TIME, it represented the basic approach of planning not only production but all types of industrial effort. It continues in use today on development-oriented programs, although in two rather specialized ways. The first is for overall *master planning* or *schedule phasing*, in which broad calendar-time goals for such a program are initially laid out. In PERT terminology, these goals represent the *scheduled time objectives,* or the T_s *concept* described in Chapter 2. As we shall see, it is the function of PERT analysis to determine if the T_s objectives are mutually consistent, if they can be met by any feasible plan, and with what degree of certainty.

The second use of the Gantt Chart today is after completion of a PERT analysis. It is then quite common to transcribe PERT information into a summary Gantt-type display. This is usually done for the benefit of executives who are unfamiliar with the network format and standard PERT reporting forms, or who prefer a calendar-time display. The special features of combined Gantt Charts and PERT networks—including the so-called "squared network"—will be discussed in Chapter 3.

So much for the basic or underlying techniques available to industry for schedule and cost control of operations through the advent of PERT. The number of variations in these basic techniques, particularly in such areas as standard cost systems, or detailed production control systems, would fill many volumes if covered in any depth. In addition, we are not considering here some of the operations research or modeling approaches to production scheduling problems, such as linear programming techniques, which evolved after World War II.[2] However, three variations of these early techniques, developed during the period of World War II for programs of a limited production nature, are of particular interest in the evolution toward PERT. These three approaches, which include the learning-curve, line-of-balance, and milestone methods, will be described later, with emphasis on their relation to PERT. For the planning and control of complex, one-time-through programs, however, and particularly those with a high degree of engineering content, the use of control systems based upon these techniques of early scientific management was marked by a notable lack of success.

Program Performance During the 1950s— RAND Study

What evidence is there to support such an assertion? The first published study of the problem, at least the first known to the author, was made by A. W. Marshall and W. H. Meckling of the RAND Corporation in 1959. In *Predictability of the Costs, Time, and Success of Development,* Marshall and Meckling studied the cost history of twenty-two major military development programs carried out during the 1950s, and the "availability" or schedule history of ten out of this same group of programs.

In the area of cost, they examined the ratio of the latest available estimate of *cumulative average cost of production* versus the earliest such estimate available, which they termed the "factor increase." The very real difficulties of making such a study are well described, but the assumptions and adjustments they were compelled to make produced, if anything, conservative results. In addition, their data cover only *production cost elements* of the twenty-two military programs studied, although it is stated in their report that "we have also compared predicted and actual development costs, and found much the same story as for production costs." [3]

Table 1 is a summary of Marshall and Meckling's data on cost

TABLE 1. TOTAL FACTOR INCREASES IN AVERAGE CUMULATIVE COST OF PRODUCTION—ADJUSTED

Fighters	Factor increase	Bombers	Factor increase	Cargoes and tankers	Factor increase	Missiles	Factor increase
1	4.0	1	4.0	1	1.6	1	6.4
2	2.5	2	2.8	2	1.5	2	6.0
3	2.0	3	1.2	3	0.9	3	2.7
4	1.5			4	0.8	4	7.1
5	2.1					5	1.3
6	1.2					6	0.8
7	0.8						
8	1.0						
9	0.6						
Mean	1.7		2.7		1.2		4.1

Mean—all classes—2.4

SOURCE: A. W. Marshall and W. H. Meckling, *Predictability of the Costs, Time, and Success of Development,* RAND Corporation Report P-1821, December, 1959.

"factor increases," after adjustments for learning-curve effects and price increases. It will be noted that cost factor increases range as high as 7.1, with the mean or average for all program classes being 2.4. In other words, the average increase in cost over original estimates for twenty-two major development programs was approximately 140 per cent, with the highest figure being approximately 600 per cent. As one would expect, the figures are higher for missile programs than for cargoes and tankers, due to the higher state of the art in development engineering involved. It is important to emphasize that these cost factor increases do not represent "overrun costs," as they are commonly understood in industry, but rather the total escalation of costs from an original base line for any and all reasons. These reasons will be discussed in a later section of this chapter.

Table 2 shows similar data for slippage in operational availability, i.e., lateness in schedule. It will be noted that the average slippage figure for ten programs was two years, with the highest figure being five years, and the average factor increase being 1.5.

TABLE 2. SLIPPAGE IN AVAILABILITY

System	Slippage, years	Slippage factors
1	5.0	2.5
2	3.0	1.6
3	3.0	1.5
4	3.0	1.5
5	2.0	2.0
6	2.0	1.5
7	1.3	1.3
8	0.7	1.2
9	0.5	1.2
10	0.3	1.1
Mean	2.0	1.5

SOURCE: A. W. Marshall and W. H. Meckling, *Predictability of the Cost, Time, and Success of Development,* RAND Corporation Report P-1821, December, 1959.

Marshall and Meckling also studied the third major parameter or measure of program success, namely, achievement of technical performance requirements. It is of particular interest to quote them on this point: [4]

Performance consists of a multitude of attributes—range, speed, altitude, reliability, maintainability, vulnerability, operability, accuracy, etc. Most of these can be quantified, but others are largely qualitative.... It is necessary, therefore, to treat estimates of performance much more broadly than estimates of cost and availability.... Among the 22 systems (studied), most fell short of performance expectations in one or more respects. Range or accuracy was sometimes less than expected. But the amount by which performance fell short was usually small in comparison to the extension of time or the increase in costs that occurred. Moreover, in some instances performance actually turned out to be somewhat better than expected. In short, though estimates of performance tend to be slightly higher than what is finally achieved, they are much more nearly fulfilled than are predictions of cost and availability.... The truth is that estimations (of cost and time) have been quite inaccurate. Cost increases on the order of 200% to 300% and extensions of development time by $\frac{1}{3}$ to $\frac{1}{2}$ are not the exception, but the rule.

Before going on to an examination of the reasons behind this very serious situation, including why earlier planning and control systems failed to help solve the problem, we will look at another important study on the subject.

Program Performance During the 1950s— Harvard Study

In 1962 Merton J. Peck and Frederic M. Scherer of the Harvard Business School published the results of a three-year research project in a book entitled *The Weapons Acquisition Process: An Economic Analysis*. In this work they analyzed the development cost and time variance factors (the same as Marshall and Meckling's factor increase) for twelve weapons programs. Their results in summarized form are shown in Table 3, where it will be noted that the average cost factor increase is 3.2, and the average time factor increase is 1.36.[5] These results are comparable with the RAND study if it is remembered that in one case production costs were involved and in the other, development costs.

TABLE 3. DEVELOPMENT COST AND TIME VARIANCE FACTORS IN
TWELVE WEAPONS PROGRAMS

Program	Development cost factor **	Development time factor ***
A	4.0	1.0
B	3.5	2.3
C	5.0	1.9
D	2.0	n.a. *
E	n.a. *	0.7
F	7.0	1.8
G	3.0	1.3
H	2.0	1.0
I	2.4	1.3
J	2.5	1.3
K	0.7	1.0
L	3.0	1.4
Average	3.2	1.36

* n.a. = not available.
** actual cost ÷ original estimate.
*** actual time ÷ original estimate.
SOURCE: Merton J. Peck and Frederic M. Scherer, *The Weapons Acquisition Process: An Economic Analysis,* Division of Research, Graduate School of Business Administration, Harvard University, Cambridge, Mass., 1962.

In addition to these twelve weapon-system programs, Peck and Scherer studied the cost and time variance factors for *commercial* programs involving a significant amount of development effort. The results are summarized in Table 4, where it will be noted that average cost factor increase is 1.7, and time factor increase is 1.4. As a result of their studies, Peck and Scherer conclude: [6]

The occurrence of cost overruns and schedule slippages apparently due to unexpected technical difficulties is by no means unique to the weapons acquisition process.... In these commercial programs schedule slippages and cost overruns were

TABLE 4. DEVELOPMENT COST AND TIME VARIANCE FACTORS IN
FIVE ADVANCED COMMERCIAL DEVELOPMENTS

Program code	Development cost factor	Development time factor
Q	2.0	1.3
R	1.8	1.9
S	1.1	1.1
U	1.8 *	1.3 *
V	1.9 *	1.3 *
Average	1.7	1.4

* Estimate before project was completed and therefore may have increased.
SOURCE: Merton J. Peck and Frederic M. Scherer, *The
Weapons Acquisition Process: An Economic Analysis,*
Division of Research, Graduate School of Business Administration, Harvard University, Cambridge, Mass.,
1962.

as common as in the weapons programs.... These results cast
doubt on the widespread belief that in the commercial world,
weapons-like variances do not occur.

These studies by RAND and Harvard generally confirm what
is well known to most government and industry personnel engaged in the execution of complex programs, whether of a development-oriented nature or not. Cost increases in excess of
100 per cent, and time slippages of up to several years, both
against original estimates, do not come as a surprise to anyone
actually engaged in the management of such programs. As has
been pointed out, the problem became particularly severe during the mid 1950s, as the number and dollar magnitude of government programs of this type increased rapidly. By the early
1960s the problem had reached such proportions, largely as a
result of the complexity and size of military and space programs,
that it became a matter of national concern. At the highest
levels of government, where "cost-effectiveness" tests are to be
applied in making decisions to authorize alternative or competing programs, it became commonplace to multiply original
program cost estimates by factors of 2 to 3. In addition, because

of overall budgeting limitations, it became increasingly necessary during this period to cancel many previously authorized programs. In 1963 Dr. Harold Brown, Director of Defense Research and Engineering, in testimony before the Congressional SubCommittee on Military Appropriations, listed fifty-seven defense programs which had been canceled during the period 1953 to 1963, on which total funds expended were $6.2 billion.

By 1962 the Department of Defense had established or endorsed a number of specific approaches in an attempt to overcome these problems. The approaches can be summarized as follows:

1. Better initial *system or program definition,* based upon components or building blocks of known feasibility
2. New cost and schedule estimating practices, i.e., *PERT/TIME and PERT/COST* analysis prior to the beginning of the development phase
3. An explicit methodology of *Configuration Management* for the acquisition phase of a program
4. *New incentive contracting approaches* to industry for the acquisition phase of a program

Each of these approaches will be discussed in the following chapters of this book, together with how they are applied to the planning and control of complex, one-time-through programs.

Reasons for Program Performance of the Fifties

What reasons can be given for these large variances from early time and cost predictions, with their admittedly unfortunate impact on planning and decision making in the national interest? The reasons most commonly advanced are as follows:

1. The great difficulty of estimating time and cost for programs with a high degree of technical uncertainty.
2. The built-in "optimistic bias" resulting from the competitive situation in which such programs are "sold." (Both government and industry are involved in this pic-

ture, together with the CPFF or Cost-Plus-Fixed-Fee contract.)

3. The lack of clear-cut technical and priority objectives, resulting in a high degree of change in program direction.
4. Problems of management planning and decision making within both industry and government, including the lack of planning and control techniques adequate for the demanding problems of modern program management.

It is generally agreed that all these factors are valid and have a significant bearing on the situation, although the relative weights assigned to them are often assessed quite differently. Peck and Scherer for instance, conclude, as a result of a statistical approach, that technological uncertainty and degree of priority factors account for only half the cost increase on the programs they studied.

Finally, it is important to note that, as a result of the developments of the 1950s and the "agonizing reappraisal" of the early 1960s, another idea has emerged with great force. This is the concept of *interdependence* of performance, time, and cost variables in complex, development-oriented programs. While not always expressed clearly, the concept implies that the relationship between these three major program variables, and particularly their impact on methods of planning and control, has much to do with the success with which such programs can be managed.

It will be the purpose of this book to suggest a methodology, based on PERT Management Systems, which will explicitly relate the three program variables of performance, time, and cost. It is clear that such a methodology, properly applied, can act as a "forcing function" in establishing more clearly defined program goals and in bringing out the problem areas associated with technical, cost, and time uncertainties in a more explicit fashion. It should be equally clear that it can never replace the manager, or substitute for any lack of ability or desire on his part to use these management techniques for their maximum benefit.

Finally, it should be clear that such a new methodology is not a replacement for the older or more conventional management systems mentioned earlier in this chapter. Rather, it represents an extension into areas of modern industry requirements where conventional systems have not worked well in the past. In fact, the new management systems can be coupled to prior planning and control approaches. For example, in the area of overall planning of corporate sales, costs, and profits, particularly for those firms engaged in complex, development-oriented programs, these new techniques can serve as an invaluable backup to aggregate program projections. In fact, such aggregate program projections are likely to be greatly in error without the benefit of the application of these techniques. In Chapter 3, the concept of coupling PERT Management Systems to overall or long-range corporate planning will be discussed further.

The Nature of Modern Programs

Before beginning to cover the specifics of PERT Management Systems, it is important to review the main characteristics of the kind of programs we are talking about, and especially to emphasize the particular characteristics which bring about the requirements for new management techniques.

We have previously suggested two major categories of such programs. These are (1) capital or construction programs which require the bringing together of many diverse elements to meet an end objective, but where all these elements are generally based on a known technology; and (2) those new-product or military and space programs which require extensive research and development to reach an end objective.

The most common characteristic of such programs is their special-purpose nature, even though in both categories there may be found some individual elements with a conventional production-volume and market-supply character. From the planning and control point of view, however, both programs have the following requirements, once the end objective (or objectives) are established:

1. The need to identify all the activities required to meet the end objective(s)
2. The need to show complex interrelationships or constraints between these activities, including organizational and technical interfaces
3. The need to predict the outcome, in time and cost, of executing all these activities, with a reasonable degree of certainty
4. The need to "optimize" or allocate limited resources in the best possible manner between activities, for the execution of the program
5. The need for flexibility, i.e., ability to update the program under conditions of change

There is an additional characteristic for research and development programs which must be emphasized, namely, the high degree of uncertainty involved. The objective of any planning technique is to minimize, or at least isolate, areas of uncertainty, but in a management system for R & D programs explicit methods for handling the uncertainty problem must be found. Along with the uncertainty, there is typically also a larger problem—scarcity of resources for R & D programs, i.e., the availability of qualified personnel to carry out such work.

There are some other aspects of development-oriented programs involving a tangible product which are worthy of mention. These include the fact that generally a unique set of drawings and bills of materials is involved, in addition to which there is a continuous flow of engineering changes to these drawings and bills of materials. Sometimes, also, these programs are characterized by a high degree of *concurrency,* i.e., overlap between the development, engineering, and production phases. These characteristics require the establishment of a management system known as *configuration identification and control,* and it is this approach, broadened into a total concept *Configuration*

Management, which will be discussed as an integral part of the new methodology in Chapter 5.

Finally, for development-oriented programs, there are some additional characteristics which have a very important bearing on effective planning and control; these include the special roles of systems engineering, reliability engineering, and value engineering, and the fact that generally low unit volume is involved, while at the same time there are very high production quality and acceptance test requirements. Chapter 5 will treat with the relationships between PERT Management Systems and these special requirements.

Interim Systems

With the history of time and cost performance which has been previously described, and the obvious difference between the characteristics of complex, special-purpose programs and conventional production programs, one may wonder why improvements in the planning and control area did not take place at an earlier date. In fact, there were steps taken in the era of World War II, although these developments were generally confined to production situations involving a medium range of volume. As we shall see, these developments involved the production of new material, such as tanks, airplanes, and radars, but not on a continuous assembly-line basis.

Line of Balance

In 1941 a graphic management control system was developed at the Goodyear Company by George E. Fouch to handle the growth of new military production programs. The approach was applied in the Navy Bureau of Aeronautics procurement program during World War II, and became known as the *line-of-balance method.* Figure 2 is an illustration of the essential elements of a line-of-balance chart.[7] At the bottom of the chart is the *program plan* or *set-back chart,* which represents the key to the line-of-balance technique. It is made up by analyzing and displaying in a horizontal fashion all the assemblies that feed into the final end product, the subassemblies that feed into these assemblies, etc., back to the point of initial purchase of material. (Item 1 on the set-back chart shows such a purchased part.) After this is done, standard or estimated times are developed for the lines connecting the start and completion points of individual assemblies and subassemblies, and the results are shown on a calendar-time scale as working days prior to shipment.

In the upper left-hand corner of the line-of-balance chart is the *objective or cumulative contract schedule.* In Figure 2 this curve shows that a total of eighty units are to be delivered by the end of the month of June. Actual deliveries are behind schedule as of the end of April. If, at the end of April, we are concerned with how many item 1 parts must be purchased in order to make delivery of all units scheduled for the end of May, we may go through the following steps:

1. Determine the set-back time to item 1 (this is twenty-four working days or one calendar month).
2. Enter the objective chart as of the date of status reporting (in this case, the end of April).
3. Go one month to the right of this date, and draw a vertical line upward to the point where it intersects the cumulative-contract-schedule line. This shows that we must have fifty-four item 1 purchased parts on order as of the end of April; otherwise the delivery quantity and schedule called for by the cumulative delivery curve will not be met.

This number, i.e., fifty-four item 1 purchased parts on order at the end of April, is carried across to the *progress* display shown in the upper right-hand portion of the line-of-balance chart. By this means a *line of balance* is developed for all items shown on the set-back chart. The value of the line of balance is always expressed in *equivalent end-product units.* For example, if two of the same parts are required for use in subas-

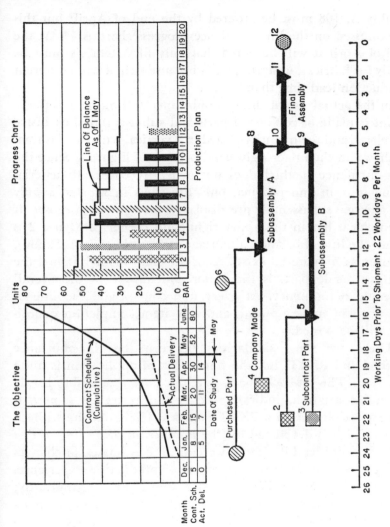

FIG. 2. Line-of-balance chart.

19

sembly A, 108 must be ordered by the end of April; but this is expressed on the line-of-balance progress chart as 54. At the end of April it will be noted that only fifty item 4's must be ready for fabrication start. This is because item 4 has a different production lead time than item 1.

In the actual use of the line-of-balance technique a periodic count is made of completed parts and subassemblies, exclusive of rejects, and the quantity posted in a vertical-bar-chart fashion, as shown in the upper right-hand portion of Figure 2. Since the line-of-balance method does not generally cover all material going into an end product, only the parts in *shortest supply* for any one subassembly are displayed for control purposes. If the vertical bar in the upper right-hand corner of Figure 2 is *below* the line of balance, a shortage of material exists; if above, an overage of material exists. As of the end of April, item 4 the company-made part, is the major contributor to the overall schedule delinquency. At every updating period the line of balance will move upward, and new item completion quantities will be posted.

There are some similarities between the line-of-balance method and PERT, but the framework of application is quite different. The set-back chart, developed from assembly breakdown information, indicates events and restraints somewhat as they are shown on a PERT network. However, the set-back chart, which is developed for the *production processing of one unit,* does not lend itself to uncertain time estimates, or changes to these estimates during the course of production experience. (If these change, the line of balance itself changes significantly; therefore the technique in its present form depends upon established standard times.) In line of balance there are no *predictive features;* i.e., there are no projections concerning potential trouble spots in the future, other than those indicated through the longest lead time by the current report. The lead time approach results in a schedule for minimum inventory rather than most economic lot size. The longest lead time on the set-back chart actually represents the largest production *cycle time,* rather than a critical path. For these reasons, i.e., lack of flexibility and predictive features, line of balance has not been used in nonrepetitive programs involving development engineering or in the early phases of production, where the product breakdown is not well defined and processing times are unstable.

There have been cases, however, where the line-of-balance method has been adapted to development programs.[8] More significant, perhaps, is the fact that, in 1963, the Federal government established a LOB Coordinating Committee, similar to the agency-wide PERT Coordinating Committee (see Figure 32, Chapter 4), for the purposes of modernizing the line-of-balance system, and studying its potentials for production costing and tie-in with PERT reporting systems.

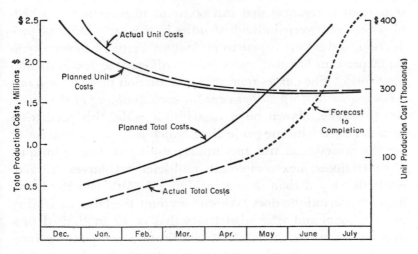

Fig. 3. Example of LOB cost display.

Figure 3 represents one way in which the line-of-balance method might be related to production cost control. For the cumulative-production-schedule line there is a corresponding *cumulative-production-cost line,* based upon unit costs predictions which are higher at the beginning of the production run. *Actual cumulative production costs* can be plotted in a manner similar to the actual delivery curve, and comparisons made against plan, along with forecasts of cost and time to complete. Whether or not problems in the cost area can be isolated to a particular subassembly or part (as they are in the quantity area) will depend on a particular company's production cost control system. In any case, if a detailed cost system and the LOB system are to be integrated into a LOB/COST system, the set-back chart will probably have to be restructured and made more comprehensive than it usually is.

Learning Curve

Another development, which basically originated in the aircraft industry prior to World War II, and which recognizes the important differences that can occur in man-hours and scheduled times between individual units in the early phase of production, is the *learning-curve technique.* Figure 4 shows a typical 80 per cent learning curve on two different scales, in its simplest form.[9] The curves represent a prediction that *unit aircraft labor costs will drop 20 per cent for each doubling of the quantity produced.* Shown on a logarithmic scale, this prediction becomes a straight-line projection, which may partially account for the widespread use and understanding of the technique. More complex, i.e., compound, multielement curves are generally developed than shown in Figure 4. Although the learning-curve technique does take into account the large variability in man-hours and scheduled times that occur in limited production situations, it does not constitute a complete or integrated program planning and control system. It is best used in projecting unit costs for a well-defined production situation, i.e., one when the unit configuration or bill of materials remains relatively stable.

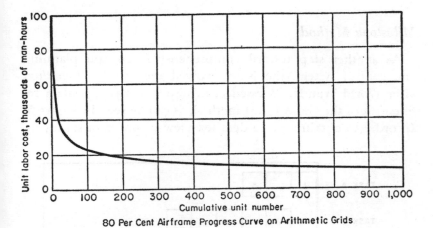

80 Per Cent Airframe Progress Curve on Arithmetic Grids

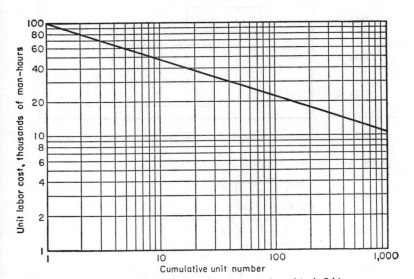

80 Per Cent Airframe Progress Curve on Logarithmic Grids

Fig. 4. The 80 per cent airframe progress curve.

23

Milestone Method

As another step toward comprehensive program planning
and control system, the Navy evolved the *milestone method*
after World War II. In essence, this approach represents a refinement of the Gantt Chart method, as can be seen in Figure 5.
In order to obtain a more detailed view of program status, in-

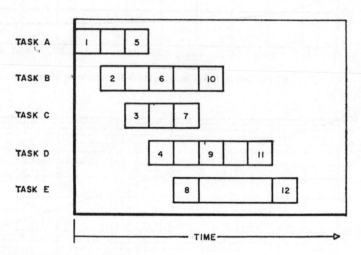

PERT NETWORK DERIVED

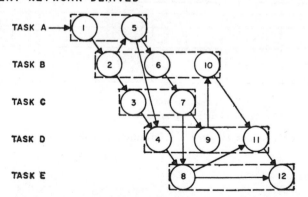

Fig. 5. Gantt milestone chart.

dividual "milestones" are called out within each horizontal bar on the Gantt Chart. To be able to monitor program progress with any improved degree of success, these milestones must represent a carefully defined point in time; this is comparable to the PERT concept of an event.

The milestone method does not explicitly indicate the constraints that exist in the program. If these constraints were shown, as indicated in the bottom half of Figure 5, a milestone PERT network would be devised. Historically, there was no concept of resource allocation or costing directly related to the milestone method. By the mid 1950s it was realized that a deeper analytical approach would be required to give any validity or predictive quality to the milestone method. Like the Gantt Chart, it has therefore tended to become a master scheduling or summary reporting technique.

Other Interim Developments

Apart from the line-of-balance, learning-curve, and milestone methods, all of which made an important contribution and can be considered predecessors of PERT, there were other developments during the 1950s which provided the foundation for the introduction of a new management system.

The development of *operations research* during World War II, and its associated modeling approaches, has been previously mentioned, and is a too extensive and well-documented subject to be covered here.[10] In industrial applications of operations research after World War II, however, the introduction of the *flow model* or *process flow diagram* as a useful way of describing industrial processes became quite common. Thus the concept of a network-like analysis or display became an established, or at least a familiar, idea. In addition, operations research or statistical approaches to the *probabilistic nature* of many industrial operations became an established concept during this same period, particularly in the areas of quality control and queuing theory. (It is interesting to note, however, that the foundations of statistical quality control go back to H. A. Shewhart of the Bell Telephone Laboratories in 1930.)

Last, and by no means least, as regards the introduction of PERT, was the development of an actual or *in-place business electronics data-processing capability.* This had happened in most large government and industrial organizations by the middle of the 1950s.

Thus the stage was set for the introduction of PERT and similar networking techniques as the basis for an integrated management system.

REFERENCES

1. E. H. Bowman and R. B. Fetter, *Analysis for Production Management,* Richard D. Irwin, Inc., Homewood, Ill., 1957, p. 56.
2. *Ibid.,* pp. 77–106.
3. A. W. Marshall and W. H. Meckling, *Predictability of the Costs, Time, and Success of Development,* RAND Corporation Report P-1821, December, 1959, p. 14.
4. *Ibid.,* pp. 20–22.
5. Merton J. Peck and Frederic M. Scherer, *The Weapons Acquisition Process: An Economic Analysis,* Division of Research, Graduate School of Business Administration, Harvard University, Cambridge, Mass., 1962, p. 22.
6. *Ibid.,* p. 433.
7. *Line-of-Balance Technology,* NAVEXOS P-1851 (Rev. 4-62).
8. *Managing a Development Program,* Bureau of Research & Development, Federal Aviation Agency, prepared by General Precision, Inc., New York, 1960.
9. Harold Asher, *Cost-Quantity Relationships in the Airframe Industry,* Project RAND, Report R-291, July 1, 1956, p. 2.
10. C. W. Churchman, R. L. Ackoff, and E. L. Arnoff, *Introduction to Operations Research,* John Wiley & Sons, Inc., New York, 1957.

2

The Fundamentals of Network Technique

Introduction

Both PERT and CPM arrived on the industrial scene at about the same time, and as essentially independent developments. Because the basic work on CPM was done in 1957, and on PERT in 1958, we shall introduce the subject of CPM first.

CPM, or the Critical Path Method, was developed by Morgan R. Walker of the Engineering Services Division of Du Pont and James E. Kelly, who was at that time with Remington Rand. Walker and Kelly were concerned with the problem of improving scheduling techniques for such projects as the building of a pilot model plant and the shutdown of a plant for overhaul and maintenance. After considering the premise that all activities of such projects must be executed in a well-defined sequence, they came up with the *arrow diagram* as the most logical representation of the interrelationships between jobs for any project. Their arrow diagram and method of calculating the longest or critical path through it are the same as the PERT network and critical-path calculation. However, Kelly and

27

014697

Walker used a *single-time estimate,* and did not go into the problem of uncertainty of time duration for individual jobs. Because CPM and PERT were independent developments, the notations of the systems are quite different, as can be seen in Table 5. Another important difference is that Kelly went on

TABLE 5. PERT VERSUS CPM NOTATION

PERT	CPM
Network	Arrow diagram
Event	Node
Activity	Job
Activity expected or scheduled time	Duration
Slack (primary)	Total float
Slack (secondary)	Free float
T_E	Earliest start
T_L	Latest start

at an early stage to develop a mathematical method for handling the problem of *expediting a project for minimum cost.* This special use of the network technique in relation to cost will be described in detail in Chapter 4.

During the period of the early development of the networking technique, Kelly,[1] * Fulkerson,[2] and Clark[3] did most of the underlying mathematical work, and their referenced papers are basic in this field.

PERT was developed in the Navy's Special Projects Office because of the recognition of Admiral W. F. Raborn that something better was needed in the form of an integrated planning and control sytem for the FBM (Fleet Ballistic Missile) program, commonly known as the Polaris Weapons System. Based upon his support, a research team was established in 1958 to work on a project designated as PERT, or Program Evaluation Research Task. By the time of the first internal Navy report on the subject, PERT had become "Program Evaluation and Review Technique," and thus it has persisted until this day,

---

* Superscript numbers indicate items listed in the References at the end of the chapter.

when it has become part of the everyday language of industry. D. G. Malcolm, J. H. Roseboom, C. E. Clark, and W. Fazar, all of the original Navy-sponsored research team, were the authors of the first publicly published paper on PERT, which was contained in the September, 1959, issue of *Operations Research*.[4] Because of the complexity and size of the Polaris program, this original research team decided to restrict the initial application of PERT to the time area, which, as it turned out, was a very wise decision.

Since these original contributions to the development and application of the network technique, the amount of literature on CPM and PERT, and the number of management systems derived from them, has increased at an exponential rate. As of 1963, any complete bibliography on PERT and CPM would have numbered entries in excess of a thousand; a representative bibliography is given by the author in Appendix 2. In addition, a compilation of the code names of the various PERT-type systems, made by the U.S. Air Force Systems Command in 1963, is given in Appendix 3. Although this compilation contains many representative entries, it is by no means exhaustive. Whether or not this confusing and to some extent unfortunate trend toward duplication and redundancy will continue remains to be seen. One example of the reversal of this trend was the withdrawal in 1962 by the Air Force of its code name PEP (Program Evaluation Procedure), which was an equivalent to PERT. In addition, the establishment by the Federal government in 1962 of a uniform Guide on PERT/COST, which will be discussed in greater detail in Chapter 4, has undoubtedly helped reduce this trend.

Basic PERT—Events

Now let us turn to the methodology of PERT/TIME, or as it now referred to, "basic or original PERT." From this point on in the book, the fundamentals of network technique common to both PERT and CPM will be discussed using PERT notation, except where there is a deviation in technique between the two systems.

Figure 6 shows a small sample network, which is taken from a larger operating network actually used in industry (in this case, the electronics industry). This sample network is representative of the lowest level of detail found in operating networks for industry development programs. This is the level at which the development and design work is actually carried out, and the activities on the network represent the "inherent" or "intrinsic" size of tasks (i.e., in terms of weeks in this work). The network therefore also represents the amount of detail required by operating-level supervision, if not by higher management. (Another restriction on level of detail will be described later under the section on Network Ground Rules.)

The ellipses on the network (they can be circles or squares) are called *events;* events are defined as being highly identifiable *points in time,* as they must be for a network to have any real meaning. For instance, Event 01, Start Project, would represent the receipt of formal authorization paper to start a project; Event 02, Complete Design Specification, would represent the completion of an approved specification in accordance with an established format and procedure; Event 08, Receive Long Lead Material, would represent the receipt and acceptance of the *last item of long lead material* needed to build a prototype. Finally, Event 09, Complete Prototype Test, would mean completion and acceptance of prototype test results, again on the basis of established or approved specifications.

Event 01 is called the *starting event* and 09 the *terminating or ending event* for this particular network as it stands. If the network in Figure 6 is considered to be a *subnetwork,* or part of a larger network, Event 09 might be called a *milestone event.* If this network is considered to be one of a group of networks, Event 09 might be called an *interface event;* in this case, the event would occur in another network with the same description and event number. In Figure 6 all events are connected by paths leading to the terminating event; if there were one event which

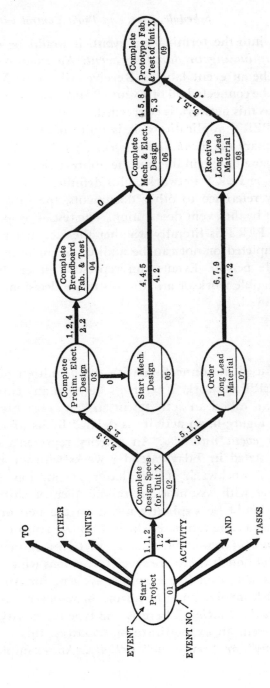

FIG. 6. Small sample network.

31

did not lead into the terminating event, it would be called a *secondary terminating or dangling event*. An example of the latter might be an event labeled Receive All Spares Material, which would be connected off of Event 08 and terminated at that point, as far as this network is concerned.

In larger PERT applications, it is quite often necessary to have a dictionary of *event definitions*. This dictionary serves the dual purpose of expanding on the abbreviations commonly used in labeling PERT networks, plus defining in a clear fashion, often by reference to other documents, the substance of what is meant by the event description. The test of proper event definition in PERT is literally whether the fact that an event has been completed or not can be audited by an independent knowledgeable person. Events can represent either the completion of tangible work or an administrative decision, such as Project Approved.

Activities

Events are used in connection with the definition of an *activity* on a PERT network. The arrow between any two events on a network is called an activity; in an "event-oriented" network such as Figure 6, an activity is defined by its *predecessor and successor event numbers*. An activity represents elapsed time, usually stated in 7-day calendar weeks with an assumed 5-day, 40-hour workweek. (This latter assumption can be changed, along with assumptions on number of shifts, etc.; but if so, it should be explicitly noted on the network.) Activities carrying a time estimate which is not zero also *represent the expenditure of resources*, usually in terms of manpower and material, although there are special situations which do not exactly fit this definition (for example, Waiting for Approval). Activities which involve an expenditure of resources are sometimes called *real activities*. There is one type of activity which does not represent an expenditure of resources; this is the so-called *"dummy"* or *"zero-time"* activity. An example of a dummy activity is shown between Events 03 and 05 in Figure 6. This dummy activity is used to indicate a constraint not requiring resources; i.e., in this particular network, it indicates that Mechanical Design work can start immediately after completion of Preliminary Electrical Design, but not until then.

Like events, activities should be well defined or understood to be useful in PERT applications. This is more difficult than might generally be imagined. In the actual construction of a PERT network, in its early phases, there is a tendency to be "event-oriented"; this has also been true in the history of PERT implementation. In order to achieve good *activity definition*, rework of "first-pass" or early event-oriented networks is sometimes necessary. This problem becomes particularly important in the application of PERT to resources or cost; in fact, for a PERT/COST application to be at all valid, the network must be worked up to a point where it is thoroughly "activity-oriented."

Network Ground Rules

There are a number of important ground rules connected with the handling of events and activities on a network. These ground rules must be followed in order to maintain the *correct topology of the network;* in addition, they have an important impact on the quality and depth of planning required to construct a network.

Ground Rule 1. Each activity must have a predecessor and successor event. Similarly, each event must have a preceding and succeeding activity, with the exception of starting and terminating events. However, an event may have *more than one* preceding and succeeding activity. In some PERT systems this latter requirement is modified; i.e., each real activity must have its own *unique* successor and predecessor event. An example of both situations is shown in Figure 7. The modified approach for handling a successor event, as shown in the right-hand portion of Figure 7, is undertaken for a number of reasons: to clarify activity and event definition; to make it easier to handle slack, scheduling, and PERT/COST Work Package problems (as will be explained in Chapter 4); and finally, in some earlier PERT applications, to make computer handling easier. The first two of these reasons have merit when applied selectively in PERT applications involving resources or cost. However, the use of the rule requiring a unique predecessor and successor

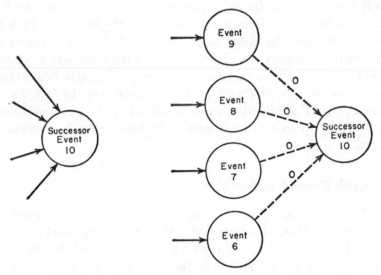

FIG. 7. Ground rule 1—effect of unique successor events.

event for each activity produces an excessive number of dummy activities, as can be seen in Figure 7. Therefore its across-the-board use is not considered advisable.

Ground Rule 2. The second basic ground rule is that no activity may start until its predecessor event is completed; in turn, no event may be considered complete until all activities leading into it have been completed. This is the key topological ground rule of the networking technique. It is the one that requires clear event and activity definition, and, in addition, a depth of analysis to uncover and portray on the network the real restraints of a program, which is not found in Gantt's technique.

It is not often recognized that this same ground rule represents one of the key criteria for determining the *level of indenture,* or amount of detail, required in PERT analysis, in addition to the inherent size of tasks mentioned previously. This point is illustrated in Figure 8, which is adapted from

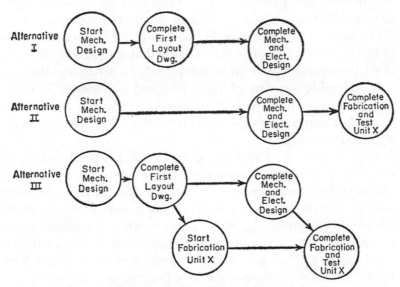

FIG. 8. Ground rule 2—effect on level of detail.

Figure 6. In Figure 6, we could have broken down the activity between Start Mechanical Design (Event 05) and Complete Mechanical and Electrical Design (Event 06) into further detail, in such a manner as shown on Alternative I of Figure 8. There is no real need to do so, however, as long as the situation portrayed in Alternative II exists, and we understand that a detailed activity such as Complete Layout Drawing is known to be contained within the definition of the original overall activity. Furthermore, we know we are at a sufficiently low level of detail if this overall activity is under the cognizance of one supervisor and is small enough for effective planning and control, in this case four weeks of elapsed time.

This situation changes, however, if we should decide to advance the Start Fabrication Unit X which begins at the Complete Mechanical and Electrical Design (Event 06). In this case we cannot talk about the Mechanical Design activity (Event 05 to 06) as being "40 or 50 per cent complete"; rather, we must isolate the *actual point in time*—in this case, the Complete First Layout Drawing—which constrains the Start Fabrication Unit X, as shown by Alternative III of Figure 8. This requirement of course, comes from the ground rule that no activity may start until its predecessor event is completed. In actual application, a considerable amount of judgment and experience is necessary to handle this aspect of networking properly, in addition to the fact that a very thorough knowledge of the subject being PERTed is required.

Ground Rule 3. This ground rule concerns the handling of *concurrent or parallel activities*. There are cases in network analysis where two or more activities can exist, in effect, between any one pair of predecessor and successor events, as shown on the left-hand portion of Figure 9. This situation sometimes comes about when technical uncertainty is involved in one of the activities, and a "backup" or "redundant" activity is added. This kind of situation will be referred to later in this chapter in connection with the use of the "Short Path Flag," and again in Chapter 6 in connection with the use of redundant activities for measuring cost uncertainty. However, as shown in Figure

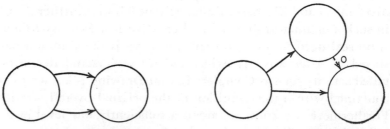

FIG. 9. Ground rule 3—Handling of parallel activities.

9, the existence of two activities between any one pair of events would produce an ambiguity, since both these activities would have the same predecessor and successor event numbers and description. The preferred method of handling the situation, which involves the introduction of a dummy activity, is shown in the right-hand portion of Figure 9.

Ground Rule 4. There is one other situation where a dummy activity is introduced; this is usually referred to as the *dependent and independent activity* situation. In Figure 10a, Activities C and D are shown as being *dependent* upon the completion of Activities A and B. It may be, however, that Activity D is *independent* of the completion of Activity A, while C is not. In this case, the preferred method of handling is shown in Figure 10b. A somewhat similar situation can occur when the results of two independent activities are to be merged together into a single follow-on activity. An example would be the com-

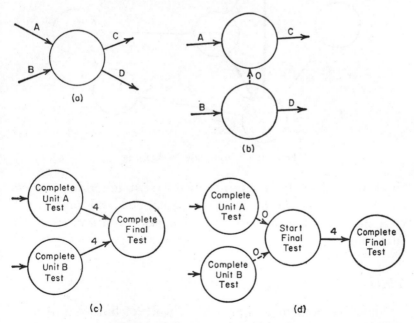

Fig. 10. Ground rule 4—illustration.

pletion of two independently developed units, which are then
to be brought together for a combined final test, as shown in
Figure 10c. The preferred version of handling this situation is
shown in Figure 10d. As will be noted, this is a situation where
judgment indicates the use of a unique starting event for Final
Test, and the introduction of two dummy activities.

Ground Rule 5. The last topological ground rule for network construction refers to the matter of *looping*. This rule
simply states that no given event can be followed by an activity
path which leads back to that same event. An example of this
is shown in Figure 11. In complex networks, and particularly

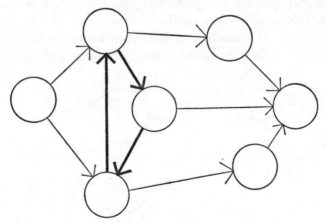

FIG. 11. Ground rule 5—looping.

those worked on by a number of different individuals or organizations, this kind of situation can happen, and most PERT
computer programs have built-in *diagnostic routines* to isolate
such loops.

Three-time Estimates

The next fundamental area of network technique which we
shall discuss concerns the matter of time estimating. After a

network configuration has been established, i.e., after all events and activities have been identified and drawn up in accordance with the previous ground rules, *elapsed-time estimates* are made for each activity. As has been stated, these elapsed-time estimates are generally made in terms of a 7-day calendar week, assuming a 5-day, 40-hour workweek. At this stage of network development, the effects of holidays and vacations are generally excluded. These are taken into account later in the *calendar scheduling process.*

In the CPM technique only a single elapsed-time estimate is made. With this approach, the problem of *uncertainty in time estimates* is disregarded, although sufficient "buried padding" may be included in the estimate to account for uncertainty. The single-time estimate works very well in such applications as construction projects, where standards exist for individual activities, or where there is a large amount of prior history on comparable activities.

In development-oriented projects there are also a good many "conventional" activities where the same condition exists; i.e., there is no significant amount of time uncertainty. The single-time approach can be used to advantage in these cases. However, there are also a good many activities, typically in the early phases of development engineering and in all testing phases, where a significant amount of time uncertainty comes to the fore during the estimating process, i.e., where no standards or comparable history exists. It was this very important problem that the original PERT research team was attempting to handle when it introduced the three-time estimating concept, which accounts for the statement that PERT is designed for programs where there are no established standards.

Unfortunately, there has been a great amount of controversy, not to mention confusion, concerning the significance and proper use of three-time estimates. Most of the opposition to their use neglects one of the fundamental principles of PERT analysis, namely, at the planning stage, it is the function of PERT analysis *to probe for areas of program uncertainty,* and to bring them out into the open for explicit analysis to the maximum extent possible.

Aside from any disagreement about the existence or non-existence of uncertainty, the major arguments against the use of three-time estimates can be summarized as follows:

1. The statistical handling of three-time estimates, i.e., their reduction to a single-valued expected time t_e and variance σ^2, can be questioned as developed in original PERT.

2. People cannot make "three-way" or even "two-way" estimates, as a measure of uncertainty, with any degree of accuracy, and that such an approach overemphasizes the "optimistic" or "pessimistic" biases of individual estimators.

3. The use of the single-time estimate is better because it places strong psychological pressure on a person to complete his work by a given date. The corollary to this argument is that most people are incapable of achieving a goal which is thought of as being of a probability distribution, or a range of possible completion dates.

Each of these arguments has a good deal of merit in it, but each also represents some misunderstanding about the role and proper application of three-way estimates in PERT. In the discussion that follows on this subject, we shall be concerned with operating-level networks, as described at the beginning of this chapter, and not with master schedules or networks, where the single-time approach is more generally used.

Let us discuss first the problems concerning the areas of statistics and accuracy of estimating. In the three-time approach, estimates are made of the *optimistic, most likely, and pessimistic* elapsed times for an individual activity, using a known level or assumed availability of resources. Interpretation of the meaning of the terms optimistic, most likely, and pessimistic has varied somewhat since their introduction in original PERT. The definitions which, in the opinion of the author, represent a useful consensus are as follows:

1. *Optimistic:* An estimate of the *minimum* time an activity will take—a result which can be obtained only if unusual good luck is experienced and everything "goes right the first time."
2. *Most likely:* An estimate of the *normal* time an activity will take—a result which would occur most frequently if the same activity could be repeated independently a number of times.
3. *Pessimistic:* An estimate of the *maximum* time an activity will take—a result which can occur only if unusually bad luck is experienced. It should reflect the possibility of initial failure and fresh start, but should not be influenced by such factors as "catastrophic events"—strikes, fires, power failures, and so on—unless these are inherent risks in the activity.

It is probably true that, if one attempts to refine these definitions with such statements as "the optimistic and pessimistic estimates can occur only one time out of a hundred," not much benefit is accrued to the individual estimator, unless he is statistically minded. It is much more important, when developing three-time estimates, to be sure that the estimator is the person who has had the most experience in the type of work involved.

Once the three-time estimates are obtained, they are thought to be connected in the form of a unimodal probability distribution, *with m, the most likely time,* being the modal or most frequent value, as is shown in Figure 12. Because *a, the optimistic time,* and *b, the pessimistic time,* may vary in their relationship to *m,* this distribution can be skewed to the left or right, as is seen also in Figure 12. It was because the *beta distribution* seemed to fit these general properties that it was chosen by the original PERT research team as the model for determining the *mean or expected time* t_e and standard deviation σ associated with the three-time estimates. After a mathematical analysis which involved an assumption of the relation-

ships between range and standard deviation, and an approximation with respect to the relationship between the mean and the
mode in the beta distribution, the PERT research team came
up with following general formulas for t_e and σ:

$$t_e = \frac{a + 4m + b}{6} \tag{1}$$

$$\sigma = \frac{b-a}{6} \qquad \sigma^2 = \left(\frac{b-a}{6}\right)^2 \tag{2}$$

THREE-TIME ESTIMATE

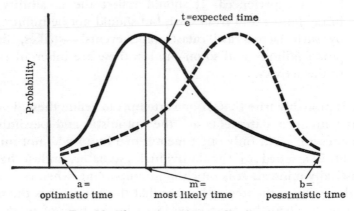

FIG. 12. Illustration of beta distribution.

For the benefit of those readers not acquainted with statistics,
t_e, *the mean or expected time,* represents a point in Figure 12
where the area under the probability curve is divided equally,
or in half. In addition, σ, *the standard deviation,* or its squared
version σ^2, *variance,* represents a measure of the dispersion or
spread of the curve. Another way of looking at these concepts is
that t_e represents the point where there is a 50-50 chance that
the actual activity completion date will be earlier or later than
t_e. The amount by which the actual date is likely to be earlier
or later than t_e will be greater with a higher value of σ.

For the interested reader, a simplified version of the complete
mathematical derivation contained in the original PERT

Phase I Summary Report is given in Appendix 1. In this Appendix, emphasis is placed on the significance of the underlying assumptions and approximations used in the original study. Suffice it to say that, though the assumptions and approximations involved in Eqs. (1) and (2) have been widely questioned (and properly so), they have also been widely used in actual practice.

In 1962 the RAND Corporation published a report in which the beta distribution assumption and errors involved in the original approximations of PERT were examined in detail.[5] In connection with the beta distribution assumption, the RAND study shows that in the context of most three-time estimating situations, where the mode falls in the central area of the range, the net error of the PERT-calculated mean was about 5 per cent of the range. With regard to the approximations given in Eqs. (1) and (2), again in the usual three-time estimating situation, and assuming partial cancellation, the errors in the mean and standard deviation reduce to 7 per cent and 4 per cent of the range, respectively. Finally, with respect to possible errors in the individual three-time estimates themselves, the net error (sum of worst positive and negative errors) is 1.6 per cent of the range. The RAND study goes on to indicate that more important than these factors is the method by which the critical path itself is calculated, and the error produced in the case of certain types of network configurations. This point will be covered later in this chapter in the section on critical-path calculations.

Statisticians will probably continue to argue, and perhaps refine, the handling of three-time estimates, and the distribution assumptions and weighting factors used in the expression for the expected time may vary. It is the author's view, however, that in practice, when there is a real concern about the problem of time uncertainty, the PERT analyst is usually drawn to an examination of the *specific optimistic and pessimistic time estimates for individual activities,* and does not explicitly use the standard deviation or PERT probability figures. In addition, the *philosophy used in the original networking effort* has a most important bearing on the validity or accuracy of time estimates obtained in PERT. An Aerospace Corporation report on this subject states the point very admirably: [6]

> The objective of using PERT is not to confine program activities within an arbitrarily fixed time span, but rather to determine the difficulty of uncertainty of performing certain activities by estimating each one separately. Then, by acting upon that series of activities which forms the critical path, tradeoffs can be made to reduce the total flow time.

In other words, if initial time estimates are based upon a predetermined schedule, rather than upon an assessment of the inherent difficulty of each activity, then the total error is likely to be greater than that resulting from any of the factors discussed above. This emphasis on a proper philosophical approach ties in very closely with psychological arguments mentioned previously. The RAND report on the small effect of individual inaccuracies in three-time estimates has been noted. In the psychological area, the answer to the arguments posed might be presented in a series of questions. If the single-time approach is used, is the result more accurate or valid in the case of uncertain activities? Do we not get some real benefit out of attempting to obtain *a measure* of the uncertainty involved —even to the extent of "calibrating" the optimistic and pessimistic biases of individual personnel? Does not the three-way estimate approach give us a much better opportunity to achieve an *honest and inherently realistic* estimate, rather than the single-time "commitment" approach, with its involved and dubious gaming model between the doer and his supervisor? [7] Finally, the argument that a person needs a single-valued goal to work against is taken care of in any complete PERT application by the actual process of scheduling itself. It should be emphasized, however, that this process of scheduling, which involves the use of a single-valued time, is only undertaken after a thorough examination of the many factors involved, including an examination of the degree of uncertainty on all activities where this is significant.

It is the author's view that the three-time estimating approach of PERT constitutes one of its most important features, since it brings the problem of uncertainty out in the open where it can be seen and evaluated. In addition, when properly used, this technique can make a significant contribution to the establishment of realistic schedules. The extension of the concept of three-time estimating to the areas of technical and cost uncertainty will be discussed later in Chapter 6.

Cumulative Expected Time—T_E

We now turn to some concepts needed for calculating the critical path (or paths) through a network, another important contribution of the PERT technique. Turning back to Figure 6, it will be noted that there are three-time estimates, given in weeks, above each activity arrow. The figures underneath the arrow are the calculated expected times t_e. We now introduce the concept of T_E, *the cumulative expected time for an event,* which represents the sum of all the individual t_e's along the path leading to that event. In calculating T_E, the *longest path leading into any one event* is the determining factor; the resulting T_E value then represents the *earliest time* that event can be completed.

This can be verified from Figure 13, which represents Figure 6 with individual T_E calculations above each event. Leading into Event 06, Complete Mechanical and Electrical Design, there are two possible paths, one with a T_E value of 4.0 + 4.2, or 8.2 (from Start Mechanical Design), and the other with a T_E value of 6.2 + 0.0, or 6.2 (from Complete Breadboard Fabrication and Test). The T_E of 8.2, being the larger of the two figures, and representing the longest path leading into Event 06, is the dominant one. The same situation exists at the final Event 09, where the reader can verify that the correct T_E is 13.5, coming in from Event 06, rather than 9.9, coming in from

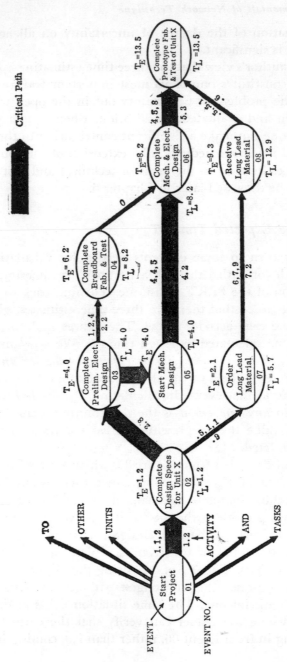

Fig. 13. Figure 5 with T_E and T_L calculations.

Event 08, Receive Long Lead Material. After calculating the T_E's for every event, which involves starting at the beginning of the network and examining all paths leading into any one event, the so-called "forward pass" through the network has been completed.

Latest Allowable Time—T_L

In PERT terminology, we can now "anchor" the network on 13.5 weeks and make the "backward pass" through the network. This is done in order to calculate T_L, the *latest allowable date for an event*. T_L represents the *latest allowable time that an event can be completed and still not disturb the completion time of the terminating event of the network*. The reader may verify, on Figure 13 where T_L figures are shown below each event, that the method of calculating T_L is just the reverse of the method of calculating T_E. At Event 03, Complete Preliminary Electrical Design, the longest *backward path* from terminal Event 09 leads through Events 06 and 05, and produces a T_L equal to $13.5 - 5.3 - 4.2 - 0$, or 4.0 weeks. The other path leading back to Event 03 is through Events 06 and 04, and is equal to $13.5 - 5.3 - 0 - 2.2$, or 6.0. It will be noted the *smaller* figure of 4.0 weeks is then chosen for T_L, since it represents the *longest* backward path. Finally, it will be noted that the value of T_L for Event 04, Complete Breadboard Fabrication and Test, is 8.2; the significance of this is that Event 04, which has a T_E of 6.2 weeks, *could* be delayed 2 weeks (until the 8.2 week) without affecting the calculated T_E of the terminating event on the network.

Critical Path

The reader will recognize that in calculating T_E we have actually traced through the longest path of the network, which is shown as a heavy line in Figure 13. This is known as the *critical* path; all other paths through this network are shorter and are therefore *subcritical.* It should be clear that if any activity along the critical path is delayed the entire program will be correspondingly delayed. This is the basis for the very important *predictive* feature of PERT, and represents its contribution to the principle of *management by exception.* It should be emphasized that if the critical path is shortened for any reason, the subcritical paths may become equal to it and therefore critical. Again, if a subcritical path is delayed, it may emerge as the critical path.

There may be *one or more* critical paths in any given network, i.e., paths with T_E values that are the same or very close to each other. In PERT analysis, particularly on larger programs, it is therefore common to examine the first *two to six critical and subcritical paths,* or all those paths that have a T_E value within several months of each other. One trend which should be watched in the management of a program under PERT control is the tendency to neglect subcritical paths, or let them slide. If this trend is allowed to go on indefinitely, all paths will tend to become critical; this process is known as "tightening up the network."

The development of a valid network, i.e., one where the configuration of events and activities is correct, the activity times are estimated on a realistic basis, and a meaningful critical path(s) results, represents a very significant accomplishment in most programs. The result often comes as a surprise to people who have judged the critical areas of a program on an intuitive basis. The achievement of such a critical-path analysis allows management to "begin to manage by exception," based upon PERT as the tool involved. We shall discuss the specifics of how this management process is carried out under the section entitled Replanning at the end of this chapter.

Meanwhile, we shall bring up one "statistical aberration" which causes an error in the calculation of critical-path values in the case of certain network configurations. It will be recalled that the T_E value of the critical path was arrived at by adding up the individual t_e's for all activities along this path; the same was true for subcritical paths. We did not discuss the possible effect of the *cumulative variance* along all these paths on the final result, even though the cumulative variance for the critical path itself may have been calculated by adding up the variance figure for all activities on it. It is important to emphasize that this simplified approach, sometimes called the *deterministic approach,* can produce a critical-path value of T_E somewhat on the low side. This problem was recognized by the original PERT research team, and more recently has been studied by a number of people, including MacCrimmon and Ryavec of the RAND Corporation.[8] In the latter study, it is shown that the amount of error depends upon the type of *network configuration* involved. If the network has many parallel paths of approximately the same length, not interconnected, as shown in the top portion of Figure 14, the error tends to be high; if the

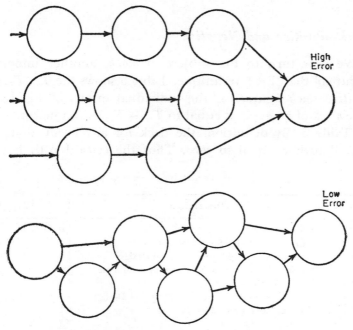

FIG. 14. Parallel and interconnected network configurations.

network has a greater degree of interconnection the error is low. It is possible to make a purely *stochastic* calculation of the network, rather than the simplifying deterministic calculation used in PERT, and thus reduce this error.[9] A more practical approach to the problem, perhaps, is the use of the figure on *probability of positive slack* for subcritical paths, which will be discussed in a later section of this chapter.

One other special aspect of the critical-path calculation is worth mentioning. In some cases, generally rare, there are a number of parallel or backup activities between any two major events; this situation was mentioned earlier in connection with events having a high degree of technical uncertainty. The *Short Path Flag* routine can be used to calculate the *shortest path,* rather than the longest path, between such major events, when it is felt that one parallel activity may be completed earlier than another.

Slack—Positive and Negative

We now turn to the subject of *slack,* another important feature of the PERT technique. Table 6 shows the T_E, T_L, and *positive slack figures* for the individual events of Figure 13. The slack of an event is equal to $T_L - T_E$, as can be confirmed in Table 6. By definition, the slack for any event along the critical path is equal to zero. Thus the critical path itself is

TABLE 6. CALCULATION OF SLACK FOR FIGURE 13

Event No.	Description	T_E	T_L	Slack
01	Start Project	0	0	0
02	Complete Design Specifications	1.2	1.2	0
03	Complete Preliminary Electrical Design	4.0	4.0	0
04	Complete Breadboard Fabrication and Test	6.2	8.2	+2.0
05	Start Mechanical Design	4.0	4.0	0
06	Complete Mechanical and Electrical Design	8.2	8.2	0
07	Order Long Lead Material	2.1	5.7	+3.6
08	Receive All Material	9.3	12.9	+3.6
09	Complete Prototype Fabrication & Test	13.5	13.5	0

said to have slack value of zero, and all subcritical paths have their individual positive slack values. The slack value of a series path is another way of expressing its criticality in the network.

When a *scheduled objective date,* or T_S, is introduced for the terminating event, then the network is "anchored" on T_S, and T_L is set equal to T_S. If T_S is *earlier* than the calculated T_E for the critical path, then we have the case of *negative slack,* i.e., the critical path is late with respect to T_S by an amount equal to $T_S - T_E$. It should be emphasized that negative slack can only exist in the case where a scheduled objective date T_S has been established which is earlier than T_E. A T_S date may be established for *other events than the terminating event;* in this case we have the possibility of more than one T_S restriction creating negative slack.

So far, we have only discussed slack with respect to an *event or path. Activity slack* has a somewhat different definition and significance. The slack value of an activity is equal to the T_L (*or T_S*) *of its successor event,* minus the activity's *individual expected time,* expressed in terms of weeks. The special significance of this can be seen in Figure 15, which shows a portion of a network taken from a larger network. The slack of Activity

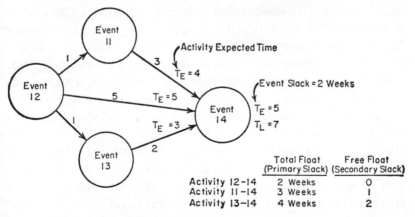

	Total Float (Primary Slack)	Free Float (Secondary Slack)
Activity 12-14	2 Weeks	0
Activity 11-14	3 Weeks	1
Activity 13-14	4 Weeks	2

Fig. 15. Illustration of activity slack and float concepts.

12-14 is 2 weeks, the same as its *successor event slack*, since this is the longest activity leading into Event 14. The slack value for Activity 11-14, however, is equal to 3 weeks, and for Activity 13-14, 4 weeks, since both these activities are shorter, or have a smaller T_E than Activity 12-14.

Thus, a number of activities leading into the same successor event can have different activity slack values as long as they have different individual activity T_E values.

It should be clear by now that the concept of positive slack, whether thought of for an event, activity, or path, represents the "degree of freedom" with which an event, activity, or path can be moved without delaying the end result of a program. Areas in the network with a high degree of positive slack do not generally require direct management attention. However, if the critical path is in a negative slack condition, it may be necessary to consider transferring manpower or dollars from the areas of positive slack to the critical path, in order to bring the program back on schedule.

Float and Secondary Slack

Before going on to a further discussion of the utilization of slack, it is important to discuss one more refinement of the concept of activity slack which is widely used in the CPM technique. In CPM, activity slack is called *float;* there are a number of kinds of float, but we shall concern ourselves with the two most important categories, namely, *total float* and *free float.* The difference between total float and free float can best be illustrated by reference to Figure 15. As was mentioned earlier, the activity slack for Activity 12-14 is equal to 2 weeks, i.e., the activity can be delayed 2 weeks before it becomes later than the T_L of its successor event (Event 14). If we were interested in the impact of this activity on the T_E *of Event 14*, however, it is clear that it cannot be moved at all. Thus, Activity 12-14 is said to have a total float of 2 weeks and a free float of 0 week.

Activity 11-14, however, has a total float of 3 weeks and a free float of 1 week; i.e., it can be delayed 1 week without interfering with the T_E of its successor event. Similarly, Activity 13-14 has a total float of 4 weeks and a free float of 2 weeks. The concept of total float versus free float has been introduced into PERT under the terms *primary slack* and *secondary slack*.

Another way of understanding the concept of free float, or secondary slack, is that it represents the amount of time an activity can be delayed, from its earliest start time, to the point where it interferes with the *earliest start time of its succeeding activity*. It is particularly important to keep these concepts in mind during the *scheduling* process; that is why the CPM approach emphasizes such information as the "earliest start" and "earliest finish," "latest start" and "latest finish" states for individual activities.

Another slack concept which is important, particularly in connection with scheduling, is the problem of *allocating positive slack*. Simply stated, this problem is: Where is the best place to schedule your slack? Should you "save it for end" where it is "safest" as a contingency factor, or should you distribute it in some other manner? There are a number of approaches to this problem, including some as sophisticated as using an *exponential coefficient* to allocate a small amount of slack at the beginning of a path and the majority of it at the end of the path. An opposite approach is to allocate the majority of the slack at the beginning of a path, on the theory that results obtained from work done in early phases of the program may make it possible to carry out later activities with greater efficiency or effectiveness. In the entire area of scheduling and allocation of positive slack, a great deal of judgment is involved in each particular case, with regard to both these factors and other factors to be discussed in Chapter 3. As will be indicated, one of the most important of these factors is manpower or loading restrictions which may result in the removal of positive slack which appears to be available.

Probability Aspects of PERT

We now come to an aspect of PERT which has been somewhat controversial ever since its inception in original PERT.
This is the concept of the *probability of accomplishing a scheduled objective date, T_S*. It will be recalled that T_S is generally
determined from an overall schedule phasing approach, and is
introduced into the situation as an *objective date*. It may also
be an arbitrary date which a high government official or top
industrial manager has set as a "challenging goal." If, after
conducting a PERT analysis, we come up with a T_E which is
later than T_S, we can talk about the *probability of meeting such
an objective date*.

The statistical argument for this calculation is as follows:
Though the distribution of possible completion times for each
activity on the critical path may vary (i.e., can be skewed from
left to right), the distribution of possible completion times
around T_E for the terminating event approximates the normal,
or bell-shaped, distribution. This assumption follows from the
central limit theorem, when there are a large number of activities on the critical path (for example, more than ten), and their
individual distributions are random. This probability situation is portrayed in Figure 16, where a terminating event is
shown with its cumulative expected time (T_E) and variance (σ^2).
In addition there are shown two possible scheduled objective
dates, T_{S1} and T_{S2}. In this situation the probability of achieving

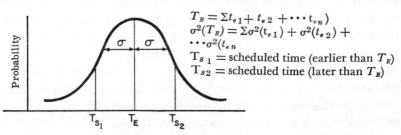

$$T_E = \Sigma t_{e1} + t_{e2} + \cdots t_{en})$$
$$\sigma^2(T_E) = \Sigma\sigma^2(t_{e1}) + \sigma^2(t_{e2}) + \cdots\sigma^2(t_{en}$$
$$T_{S1} = \text{scheduled time (earlier than } T_E)$$
$$T_{S2} = \text{scheduled time (later than } T_E)$$

Fig. 16. Probability of meeting a scheduled objective date T_S.

a T_S is defined as the ratio of the area under the curve *to the left of* T_S to the area under the *entire curve*. The value of this probability is found most quickly by expressing the difference between T_S and T_E in units of σ, i.e.,

$$\frac{T_S - T_E}{\sigma}$$

and entering the result into a normal probability distribution table. This final result will yield a value for the probability of accomplishing T_S. Thus

$$\frac{T_{S1} - T_E}{\sigma} = -1.2\sigma \qquad \text{Pr. (accomplishment of } T_{S1}) = 0.12$$

$$\frac{T_{S2} - T_E}{\sigma} = +1.2\sigma \qquad \text{Pr. (accomplishment of } T_{S2}) = 0.88$$

The use of this probability figure by personnel who do not understand the underlying statistical assumptions and significance can be very misleading. For example, it is possible to have a low probability figure in a case when activity times are estimated to be quite certain and therefore the cumulative variance figure is quite small. This will yield a low probability figure in a situation where the expected date is less than a month behind the scheduled date. In general, it is the *magnitude* of the difference between T_S and T_E, expressed in terms of months or weeks, which is of greater interest to the decision maker than the PERT probability figure. Another way of saying this is that the decision maker will be interested in the amount of projected negative slack.

If there are a number of paths of approximately equal slack value, the analyst will be interested in another probability figure, previously mentioned in connection with the discussion on critical path. This is *probability of positive slack for a given path*, shown in Figure 17. Here we see the probability distribution around both T_E and T_L for the ending event on a path which has an expected positive slack value. We see that in the shaded area, where the T_L distribution curve crosses over the

T_E distribution curve, there is a chance that no positive slack will exist. This concept allows the *ranking of paths* in terms of their probability of positive slack which is equal to 1 minus the probability of no positive slack, or $P_S = 1 - P_{NS}$. Recent PERT/ TIME computer programs, such as the Air Force System Command PERT III Computer Program, provide this figure for the analyst. An example of the manual calculation of this figure

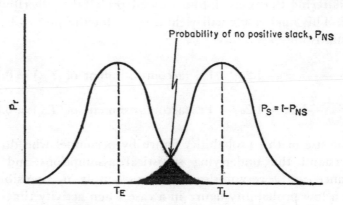

FIG. 17. Illustration of probability of positive slack P_S.

may be found in Army Materiel Command Regulation 11–16 on Planning and Control Techniques for Project Management.[10]

Replanning

Now that the fundamentals of basic PERT/TIME have been covered, the reader unfamiliar with the technique may well ask: What happens if the T_E and T_S for a terminating event are far apart, and there exists a figure which shows a high degree of negative slack, or low probabilities of accomplishment or positive slack?

In the opinion of the author, the answer to this question also constitutes one of the fundamental features of the PERT technique, though it is not often understood or treated as such. A negative slack condition obtained after completion of a first-pass network and PERT analysis is by no means unusual; it is the rule not the exception. In fact, some government agencies experienced in the evaluation of PERT networks take explicit recognition of this fact. If there is no negative slack resulting from the first PERT analysis, it is understood that the network was probably poorly developed, or may have even been "rigged."

The answer to this apparent dilemma of PERT lies in *replanning the network*. There are three basic ground rules which can be legitimately applied to the replanning of a network to meet a T_S objective. A fourth, if somewhat obvious, ground rule is that time estimates along the critical path cannot be merely adjusted to meet the T_S date. Experience has shown that if a PERT network is developed with the proper approach, and to a low enough level of detail, the first estimates made of activity times are as good as any, and should not arbitrarily be adjusted to meet a scheduled date.

The three basic ground rules for replanning the critical-path areas of a network are as follows:

1. *Change series activities to parallel.* This is the "concurrency" approach which may involve a "risk trade-off" which has to be evaluated by the manager. An example of this approach was shown in Alternative III of Figure 8.

2. *Apply additional resources to susceptible activities* (overtime, better people, etc.). In some cases, such as in common drafting and shop areas, it is fairly easy to transfer additional personnel from positive slack activities. In other cases, where personnel cannot be easily transferred, or are not available, new personnel and/or funds will have to be obtained.

3. *Delete activities* (change scope of work, i.e., delete part of an environmental test, etc.). Though generally not as easy, this approach can and has been used where time is of paramount importance.

It should be emphasized that these ground rules must be applied to specific activities in an explicit manner; a generalized approach to replanning is not considered acceptable in PERT. When a network has been replanned in accordance with these rules, so that it meets or comes as close as possible to meeting the scheduled date T_s, the application of "basic" or "fundamental" PERT/TIME planning and analysis has been completed. The words planning and analysis are emphasized; in Chapter 3 we shall discuss the problem of converting the plan to a schedule. We shall also deal with many problems of implementing PERT/TIME successfully, along with pros and cons concerning where and how it can be best applied.

REFERENCES

1. J. Kelley, "Critical Path Planning and Scheduling: Mathematical Basis," *Operations Research,* vol. 9, no. 3, pp. 296–321, May–June, 1961.
2. D. Fulkerson, "A Network Flow Computation for Project Cost Curves," *Management Sciences,* vol. 7, pp. 167–178, 1961.
3. C. Clark, "The Optimum Allocation of Resources Among Activities of a Network," *Journal of Industrial Engineering,* vol. 12, pp. 11–17, January–February, 1961.
4. D. G. Malcolm, J. H. Roseboom, C. E. Clark, and W. Fazar, "Application of a Technique for Research and Development Program Evaluation," *Operations Research,* vol. 7, no. 5, pp. 646–670, September–October, 1959.
5. K. R. MacCrimmon and C. A. Ryavec, *An Analytical Study of the PERT Assumptions,* RAND Corporation Memo RM-3408-PR, December, 1962.
6. E. T. Bobak, *The Design, Implementation, and Operation of a PERT System on a Space Program,* Aerospace Corporation Report TDR-930 (2408) TR-2, February, 1962.
7. E. O. Codier, *PERT Application at LMED,* General Electric Company, 1960.
8. MacCrimmon and Ryavec, *op. cit.*
9. D. R. Fulkerson, "Expected Critical Part Lengths in PERT Networks," *Operations Research,* vol. 10, no. 6, pp. 808–818, November–December, 1962.
10. AMCR 11–16," Planning and Control Techniques for Project Management," vol. II, pp. 3.34–3.35, August, 1963.

3

PERT/TIME Implementation

Introduction

In Chapter 2 the basic techniques and methodology of PERT/TIME were discussed. We now turn to the important factors involved in actually implementing the technique. The introduction of PERT/TIME into an organization can have many problems associated with it, particularly if the organization has not previously been accustomed to detailed planning effort. The problems of implementing PERT/TIME can be divided into two major categories, namely, psychological and technical. After these problems and the recommended strategies for resolving them have been discussed, additional pros and cons and areas of application of PERT will be covered.

Psychological Problems

The first problem in any successful PERT inplementation is to motivate the organization to carry out the detailed planning effort involved. Except where a tradition of detailed planning has previously existed, such as in well-organized production operations, there is generally great resistance to the introduction of PERT. This resistance can occur at all levels of the organization, from top management down to the lowest-skill-level personnel assigned to a program.

Top Management Viewpoint

We shall first discuss some common viewpoints of top management with respect to the introduction of PERT. These are expressed in terms of a series of statements by the executive involved in a decision on PERT, followed by a discussion of the stated viewpoint:

1. "The ability of our organization to carry out project work has been, and continues to be, good. Therefore, we see no need to introduce a new management system such as PERT." If this viewpoint is sustained by objective analysis, i.e., the organization has a better-than-average record in planning and controlling project work, there would be no apparent justification for introducing a new management system such as PERT. It will be recalled from Chapter 1, however, that in both military and commercial fields the bulk of evidence suggests that industry *as a whole* has a major management problem in this area. (See the RAND and Harvard studies on program performance during the 1950s in Chapter 1.) Even if a company has enjoyed an outstanding record relative to competition, it will probably want to introduce PERT in order to stay ahead of competition, or participate in government-sponsored programs where PERT is a program reporting requirement.

2. "Government requirements for PERT reveal detailed information which is properly kept within the province of industry." This problem has been one of major concern to management in the defense and space industries ever since the introduction of PERT on the Polaris program in 1958. In Chapter 1 the reasons why the Federal government felt it necessary to introduce a new program planning and control technique

were discussed. Unfortunately, in the early applications of PERT, there was a tendency for the government to request submission of information on individual activities from detailed PERT networks. This information was required as input data for processing in government computers. However, this situation changed as industry acquired the ability to handle PERT computer processing internally and to produce appropriate higher-level output reports. As of 1963, the policy of most government agencies was to require only certain top-level reports, such as the Management Summary Report specified in the *DOD/NASA Guide* of June, 1962. This change in government policy is based upon the assumption that any company doing contract work has an established internal capability to handle PERT Management Systems. However, the computer programs used must be compatible with, or produce the outputs required by, the government agency involved.

3. "The cost of implementing PERT/TIME, including its impact on our operating organization, is an unknown, or it is too high for us to afford it." As of 1963, the results of several studies indicate that the cost of implementing PERT/TIME ranges from 0.2 to 1.0 per cent of total program cost. This figure will vary with such factors as the size of project involved, the prior company experience or lack of experience in detailed planning, and the amount and quality of PERT indoctrination given. Suffice it to say that the costs of implementing PERT in an organization which has not previously done detailed program planning may initially be quite high; yet this may be the very case where its introduction will produce the greatest benefit. It should be emphasized that the figure of 1.0 per cent does not represent *additional or incremental cost*. To determine incremental cost, we would need to know the cost of prior planning methods, such as the Gantt technique, and this is usually difficult to determine. It is clear that PERT will, at least initially, cost more than prior methods because of the greater depth of planning involved. A common estimate is that PERT costs twice as much as conventional planning methods. It remains

for management to assess whether or not the introduction of PERT will, for this additional cost, produce a net payoff.

The gains to be achieved with PERT in terms of both tangible and intangible benefits are summarized as follows:

1. A basic improvement in planning, in terms of more realistic time estimates (and with PERT/COST, cost estimates), which allow for better decision making prior to entering upon new programs. It is commonplace for programs to be approved on the basis of optimistic or unrealistic estimates, only to be terminated at a later date when the true facts emerge. This situation produces severe waste of any company's resources.

2. A greatly improved ability to control programs against original objectives, through early detection of uncompleted events and isolation of important problem areas by means of critical-path analysis. In other words, the possibility exists of executing complex programs within plus or minus 20 per cent of original estimates, rather than the large increases in cost and time that were indicated in Chapter 1.

3. Potential for actual cost savings, increases in efficiency, and improvement in profits. These include such savings as the selective use of overtime on critical-path activities, rather than "crashing" a whole department; or shortening total project time through network analysis and replanning. In the latter case, many tangible "downstream" savings can be achieved which are not directly related to the project effort being PERTed. An example is a combined engineering and production program where the engineering release is made on schedule, or earlier than schedule, thus allowing production buyers more time to negotiate better prices. When PERT is used in the areas of plant construction, maintenance, and overhaul, significant profit gains have been reported because of earlier schedule completion. These gains involve minimizing production stoppage, or earlier entry of a new product into the market. Specific examples of the profit improvements achieved are given in Chapter 6.

Thus, for the kinds of programs where PERT is applicable, the question management may well ask itself is not "Can we afford PERT?" but "Can we afford not to have it?"

Operating Personnel Viewpoint

We shall next discuss the viewpoints of operating-level personnel, i.e., personnel assigned to manage or carry out the work of a specific program, because they are often quite different from those of top management.

A standard argument used by these people against PERT, particularly when its application for research and development programs is proposed, is that "you can't schedule invention." It has been emphasized that PERT is not used in the context of a program involving pure research or basic invention. Rather, it is most usefully applied in the case where the *end objectives* of a program are well defined. Generally speaking, a program without such objectives is unPERTable; and conversely, if objectives have been established, it is rational to assume that a plan can be developed for achieving them. The uncertainties that exist in achieving these objectives can be handled by the judicious use of three-time estimates on individual PERT activities. In addition, the use of PERT allows for flexibility in updating the program plan and rapid determination of the impact of any new changes in the plan. When PERT is explained in this frame of reference, a primary basis of objection to it on the part of operating personnel is often overcome.

A more basic objection on the part of operating personnel involves their unwillingness to provide higher management with a detailed plan, or even to carry out any detailed planning at all. It is a wise management that knows how to insist on, and obtain, detailed plans from operating personnel, and yet not use the results of such planning in a punitive manner. It is also a wise program manager who understands the contributions a system like PERT can make to the effective management of his own program. These include:

1. A better visualization of the individual tasks to be accomplished. If operating personnel participate in the development of networks, as they should in any proper PERT implementation, their understanding of not only their own tasks but their place in the entire program is significantly increased. The advantages in improved communications, particularly in large organizations, or between organizations, can be very significant.

2. The establishment of interim schedule objectives. These are much more meaningful to subordinate operating personnel than longer-term schedule objectives.

3. A clearer delineation of responsibilities, not only for the execution of detailed tasks, but for key decision-making events. A project manager who requires a top management or customer decision by a certain date in order to manage his program effectively is well advised to indicate this fact on his PERT network.

The best approach toward motivating an organization to implement PERT/TIME has often been the subject of argument. Since, based upon historical experience, the most general use of PERT is at the project operating level, it has been argued that PERT should be introduced from the bottom up, and not by management edict. The counterargument is that PERT will not be carried out effectively unless it receives the full endorsement and backing of top management. As we have seen for many companies in the defense and space industry, this particular problem has been resolved by the government's requiring the use of PERT in the execution of contracted programs. In the author's view the problem of motivating the organization to first applications of the technique is best handled by a combination of the bottom-up approach and top management endorsement.

Technical Problems

Having covered the basic methodology of PERT/TIME, and assuming that the organization is motivated to use it, we now turn to some technical problems—or more properly, problems of technique—involved in making an actual application. The approach to proper organization for handling PERT Management Systems will be discussed later in Chapter 6.

After achieving proper motivation, the method by which one goes about applying PERT, including flexibility in approach to problems peculiar to a given project, has more to do with success of implementation, and answering the pros and cons of PERT, than any other single factor.

Initial Planning

The PERT analyst or coordinator is well advised to organize the first "official" PERTing session on a formal basis, and to prepare himself in a special fashion prior to this meeting. This preparation includes the development of a *Work or Task Breakdown Structure,* and the determination of those persons in the organization who will either be responsible for or actually execute the individual tasks of the program.

Figure 18 shows a typical Work Breakdown Structure, where the major tasks of the program are organized in a pyramid-like fashion from the highest to the lowest level. It will be noted that the Work Breakdown Structure is largely *product- or hardware-oriented.* In this sense it is comparable to what is often called a unit, assembly, or drawing breakdown sequence. There are certain to be major tasks in the Work Breakdown Structure which do not fit this sequence, however. These include engineering of an assembly which is common to more than one unit in the Work Breakdown Structure, or integration of more than one unit into an entire system. There are also certain to be "nonhardware" tasks, such as the production of parts lists, handbooks, and other documentation. An illustration of how these problems may be handled on a Work Breakdown Structure for a larger program is given in Figure 33, Chapter 4. After reviewing all information available on the requirements of the program, the PERT analyst must exercise his best judgment in

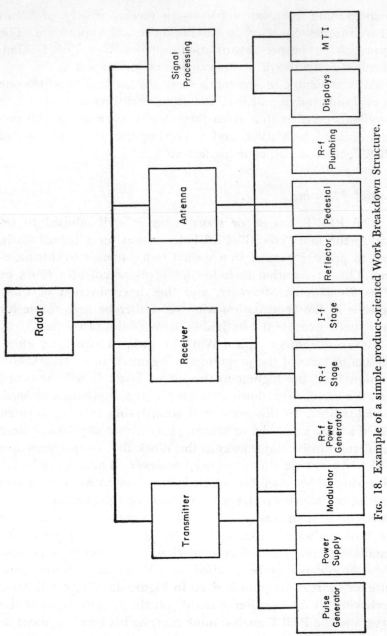

FIG. 18. Example of a simple product-oriented Work Breakdown Structure.

displaying all tasks at the proper "level of indenture" on the Work Breakdown Structure. He may do this in a preliminary fashion, working with the systems engineers involved, or he may make it the first order of business at the official PERT meeting. In any case, the Work Breakdown Structure having all major tasks together with the technical or performance specifications for the lowest-level boxes on it—sometimes call the *End Item Subdivisions*—should be understood before actual PERTing begins.

Establishing the Work Breakdown Structure is a most important first step and, on larger programs, may not even be possible until a formal Systems Definition phase has been accomplished, as will be discussed in Chapter 5. The concept of the Work Breakdown Structure for initial "top-down" planning has been widely discussed in PERT literature; however, the importance of defining the *substance of the work* involved in each End Item Subdivision, in terms of performance specifications, has often been neglected. In effect, the degree to which the End Item Subdivisions of a Work Breakdown Structure are defined is a reflection of the degree to which the end objectives of the program are understood. For example, such an End Item Subdivision as the r-f power generator shown in Figure 18 would not be ready for PERTing unless typical end objectives —such as power output and frequency, including tolerances around them—were clearly defined.

The next thing the PERT analyst needs to determine prior to a first PERT meeting is what personnel or organizational units will be involved in each End Item Subdivision of the Work Breakdown Structure. At this point he may wish to go as far as establishing a formal *Task Matrix,* as shown in Figure 19, which relates the End Item Subdivisions to the elements of the organization which will perform the work. It should be remembered that the Work Breakdown Structure is generally *not equivalent* to the company's organizational structure; the development of the Task Matrix represents the conversion table between the two. In addition, the Task Matrix should show any

major tasks which are to be subcontracted, or performed outside the organization. These tasks may require individual
PERTing with subcontractor personnel. Much of the work in
developing the Task Matrix may be done prior to the first
PERT meeting, or, again, it may represent the second order
of business. On smaller programs it may not be necessary to
establish a formal Task Matrix, since the process of actual net-

Tasks	Design Department			Drafting		Shops	
	Section A	Section B	Section C	Layout	Detailing	Fabrication	Assembly
Pulse Generator		X		X	X.	X	X
Power Supply	X			Outside	Purchase		◡
Modulator	X	X		X	X	X	X
R-f Power Generator	X	X		X	X	X	X
R-f Stage		X		X	X	X	X
I-f Stage		X		X	X	X	X
Reflector			X	X (Prel)	Outside	Purchase	
Pedestal			X	X (Prel)	Outside	Purchase	
R-f Plumbing	X	X		X	X	Outside	Purchase
Displays		X		X	X	X	X
MT I		X		X	X	X	X

FIG. 19. Example of a simple Task Matrix.

working against the End Item Subdivisions will identify all
organizational units responsible for carrying out each activity.

One further point is worth emphasizing is the area of task-
oriented versus organizational- or functional-oriented approaches to networking. If the network is developed against a
functionally based structure, rather than a Work or Task
Breakdown Structure, there are likely to be many restraining
or dummy activities, and the network will appear more confusing. This is the disadvantage of the so-called "functional-
banding" approach applied at lower organizational levels. This
complexity in networking results from the fact that most tasks

are executed by, and move through, many functions in the lower levels of the organization, as shown by the Task Matrix, Figure 19.

Armed with the Work Breakdown Structure, the Task Matrix, and a knowledge of the end objectives and/or deliverable items of the program, the PERT analyst is ready to begin the PERTing effort. He will generally lead not only a first working session, but a number of such sessions, until the first-pass network is complete. These sessions ideally include all the personnel involved on at least a particular End Item Sub-division. During the actual process of PERTing, the analyst may work on a large sheet of transparent paper or a blackboard, or he may use any one of a number of mechanical or magnetic devices that are available commercially for displaying network information. If all the personnel participating in the effort are well prepared, in addition to being properly indoctrinated in PERT, a 100- to 200-event first-pass network may be developed in a day's time or less.

During the process of networking, the PERT analyst must keep in mind at all times that the objective is to come up with a network that will be *meaningful to the persons* who will ultimately carry out the work. The emphasis on this principle, together with the proper use of ground rule 2 discussed in Chapter 2 (i.e., the display of all necessary activity restraints or interconnections), will largely determine the amount of detail involved in the PERTing exercise. Thus the PERT analyst must use good judgment in maintaining a proper balance between the conflicting requirements of simplicity of networks and a depth of analysis which will yield meaningful results.

Other ground rules which the PERT analyst should follow during initial PERTing are:

1. Do not work on calendar-scaled paper at this point—this is likely to produce *schedule biasing* when time estimates are made.

2. Establish the *configuration of the network first* (i.e., events and activities and their interconnections), working from right

to left, left to right, or from the middle outward—whichever produces the best results in the most efficient fashion for the particular personnel involved.

3. Keep in mind that the philosophy at this point should be bottom-up, not top-down. The objective of initial PERTing is to probe areas of uncertainty and discuss possible alternative paths before a final choice is made. The use of *model networks* at this point can be an aid; they may save time and provide more consistency in the overall network. However, the analyst should remember that PERT is best applied to, and in fact was developed for, *nonstandard situations,* and that model networks should therefore be used with great caution. One of the jobs of the PERT analyst is to probe continually for new factors in the particular program at hand, as compared to prior programs.

4. If he wishes to obtain quick first-pass results, the PERT analyst may emphasize event orientation in initial networking. However, he should always keep in mind that the final objective is to develop a network which is activity-oriented, i.e., one in which the individual activities are thoroughly understood by the personnel who will make time estimates. He may wish to use *unique* start and complete events to identify some activities clearly, as was described under ground rule 1 in Chapter 2. He will want to make sure that there is an event for all *deliverable items,* and that all *interface events,* i.e., events connecting with other networks or organizations, are identified. He should also call out all significant decision-making or approval events which are the responsibility of higher management or the customer. He has the problem of making sure that all major interconnection points are properly "formatted" on the network, and that the network terminates in a clear and comprehensible manner.

After the network configuration has been established in accordance with the above ground rules, elapsed-time estimates should be made for each activity. As has been mentioned, the three-time estimate should be used whenever there is any degree of time uncertainty. *Schedule biasing* should be minimized during the time estimating process by not examining T_S dates for any event until after its T_E has been calculated. It is possible at this stage to have the time estimates reflect special loading conditions, particularly where such a restraint is clearly understood. For example, there may be only one team of technical personnel capable of carrying out a particular installation and test activity which is repeated at various geographical locations. Another example would be the restrictions caused by the use of a special-purpose testing facility. These kinds of loading restraints can be indicated, even in a first-pass network, and represent an example of how PERT analysis should be conducted with a flexible approach and the use of good judgment.

Computer or No Computer

After the initial networking session has been completed, the analyst is well advised to establish the time for a follow-up meeting, which will involve a review of calculations and replanning the network. In order to maintain a high interest level on the part of all personnel concerned, this follow-up meeting should be held within a few days of the final networking session, at the latest.

In the interim, the analyst must "clean up and code up" the network. At this point he establishes a code for each event (or activity) on the network, in accordance with his own company procedures, or any specific government requirements. Among the factors to be considered in establishing a proper event coding structure are:

1. The analyst should keep the number of digits within a reasonable limit, such as a maximum of nine digits.

2. In establishing the code number, the analyst has the option of identifying "lower-level" information, such as Work Order or Work Package number and organizational element, particularly if the application is to be extended into PERT/COST.

Generally speaking, however, organization information is already carried in the company's basic source document for time charges, and it is not necessary or desirable to have the event code structure identify Work Order numbers. The same is true of the identification of "higher-level" information, such as End Item Subdivision numbers and Work Breakdown Structure level numbers. These need not be coded into the basic event number if there are provisions for summarizing to them, or making separate entries for them on PERT input documents. It is sometimes desirable, however, particularly on larger programs, to have the event code structure relate to *network identification* and event *"shred-out" level* if there is no separate provision for handling them. The event shred-out level should be distinguished from the Work Breakdown Structure level. The former involves the selection of particular events in a detailed network for shred-out and special-purpose higher-level reporting. In larger programs, this shred-out or event level coding is not necessarily related to the level coding of the Work Breakdown Structure hierarchy and is, in fact, often specified by the customer. Another special requirement often established by the customer is for the coding of *interface events* between networks. As we shall see at the end of this chapter, these interface code numbers will be used for the special purpose of network integration. An example of how both these customer coding requirements are handled is shown in the two columns after Beginning Event Number in Figure 20.

3. As a practical matter, event numbers can be established on a random basis, since most computer PERT processing routines can handle random code numbers. This approach allows for flexibility with updating of networks. It is often desirable, however, particularly in the case of manual processing, to code events in sequence down a given path or chain on the network, as a convenience in later analysis of slack paths. As a general rule, the analyst should keep in mind that it is not desirable to build too much identification into his event code numbering structure.

PERT TIME INPUT FORM

SECURITY CLASSIFICATION

INITIAL CARD

REPORT DATE: 15 JUL 63

NETWORK START DATE: 07 15 63

OUTPUT HEADING: SAMPLE FAIRWEATHER MISSILE CORP

USER'S SYMBOL: A S O E P

SYSTEM OR PROJECT NUMBER: 0802264

ACTIVITY CARD

BEGINNING EVENT NUMBER	ENDING EVENT NUMBER	OPTIMISTIC TIME	MOST LIKELY TIME	PESSIMISTIC TIME	SCHEDULED OR COMPLETED DATE	ACTIVITY TITLE
34,2,1,0,0,0,1	0,0,0,1			0,7,1,5,6,3	FMC START 1ST OPER UNIT
0,0,1	0,0,2	0,0,1,0	0,0,3,0	0,0,6,0	FMC START MAINT EQUIP FAB
0,0,1	0,0,3	0,0,5,0	0,0,7,0	0,0,8,0	FMC START MISSILE TRANSP VEH FAB
0,0,1	0,0,4	0,0,1	0,0,2	0,0,0,5	FMC START MISSILE FAB
0,0,1	0,0,5	0,0,1,0	0,0,3,0	0,0,6,0	FMC START MISSILE ERECT EQUIP FAB
0,0,1	0,0,6	0,0,4,0	0,0,5,0	0,0,6,0	FMC START EMPLACE EQUIP
0,0,1	0,0,7	0,0,1,0	0,0,2,0	0,0,8,0	FMC START MAINT PERS TRAINING PLAN
0,0,1	0,0,8	0,0,3,0	0,0,4,0	0,0,5,0	FMC START SITE CONSTRUCTION
0,0,1	0,0,9	0,0,1	0,0,2	0,0,0,5	FMC START GRD EQUIP FAB
0,0,1	0,1,0	0,0,1,0	0,0,2,0	0,0,0,5,0	FMC START INSTAL C-O EQUIP FAB
0,0,1	0,1,1	0,0,3,0	0,0,4,0	0,0,5,0	FMC START TRAINING OPER PERS
0,0,2	0,2,7 A	0,1,4	0,1,9	0,0,2,4,0	FMC MAINT EQUIP AVAILABLE

SECURITY CLASSIFICATION

Fig. 20. Sample PERT input data.

73

After coding, the network is checked to see that there are no obvious errors, such as looping. The analyst then has the option of calculating the network manually or by using a computer, depending upon the size and complexity of the network. If the network is less than one hundred events, and does not have too many complex interconnections, the analyst should be able to calculate typical PERT data of the type shown in Table 6 of Chapter 2 within a matter of hours. Thus, the small business organization that wishes to participate in defense and space programs, or to improve its own internal schedule planning and controls, should not hesitate to adopt the PERT/TIME system merely because it does not possess large-scale data-processing equipment.

If the network is large and complex, the analyst may wish to obtain first-pass T_E and T_L calculations, as well as a full set of PERT/TIME slack data, by means of a computer run. In order to do so, input cards of the type shown in Figure 20 must be made up. The details of the input cards vary with the particular PERT/TIME system and computer program involved.

After the computer run has been made and debugged, the analyst will have at least three basic reports which are commonly available in PERT/TIME computer outputs. These three reports, which are shown in Figures 21 to 23, are the *Slack Order, Event Code Number Order, and Expected Date Order Reports.*

DATE 06/16/63		PERT SYSTEM		SEQUENCE: SLACK	
EVENT	NOMENCLATURE	EXPECTED DATE	LATEST ALLOWABLE DATE	SCHEDULE DATE	SLACK
01-173	CHECK DETAILS	09/23/63			-14.0
01-175	DETAILS APPROVED	10/07/63			-14.0
01-176	ENGINEERING RELEASE	10/21/63			-14.0
01-154	DETAILS APPROVED	08/26/63			3.0
01-156	ENGINEERING RELEASE	09/10/63		09/30/63	3.0
01-133	PURCHASING SPEC. REVISED	09/07/63			7.0
01-134	PURCHASING SPEC. REVISION APPROVED	09/15/63			7.0
01-135	ENGINEERING RELEASE	09/20/63			7.0
01-138	FINAL DESIGN INFO. TO VENDOR	10/07/63			7.0
01-130	COMPL. LAYOUT REVISION	08/19/63		11/04/63	10.0
01-131	LAYOUT APPROVED	08/26/63			10.0

FIG. 21. PERT computer readout report—slack sequence.

DATE 06/16/63			PERT SYSTEM	SEQUENCE:	EVENT	
EVENT	NOMENCLATURE	EXPECTED DATE	LATEST ALLOWABLE DATE	SCHEDULE DATE	SLACK
01-130	COMPL. LAYOUT REVISION	08/19/63		11/04/63	10.0
01-131	LAYOUT APPROVED	08/26/63			10.0
01-133	PURCHASING SPEC. REVISED	09/07/63			7.0
01-134	PURCHASING SPEC. REVISION APPROVED	09/15/63			7.0
01-135	ENGINEERING RELEASE	09/28/63			7.0
01-138	FINAL DESIGN INFO. TO VENDOR	10/07/63			7.0
01-154	DETAILS APPROVED	08/26/63			3.0
01-156	ENGINEERING RELEASE	09/10/63		09/30/63	3.0
01-173	CHECK DETAILS	09/23/63			-14.0
01-175	DETAILS APPROVED	10/07/63			-14.0
01-176	ENGINEERING RELEASE	10/21/63			-14.0

FIG. 22. PERT computer readout report—event sequence.

DATE 06/16/63			PERT SYSTEM	SEQUENCE:	EXPECTED DATE	
EVENT	NOMENCLATURE	EXPECTED DATE	LATEST ALLOWABLE DATE	SCHEDULE DATE	SLACK
01-130	COMPL. LAYOUT REVISION	08/19/63		11/04/63	10.0
01-131	LAYOUT APPROVED	08/26/63			10.0
01-154	DETAILS APPROVED	08/26/63			3.0
01-133	PURCHASING SPEC. REVISED	09/07/63			7.0
01-156	ENGINEERING RELEASE	08/10/63		09/30/63	3.0
01-134	PURCHASING SPEC. REVISION APPROVED	09/15/63			7.0
01-173	CHECK DETAILS	09/23/63			-14.0
01-135	ENGINEERING RELEASE	09/28/63			7.0
01-138	FINAL DESIGN INFO. TO VENDOR	10/07/63			7.0
01-175	DETAILS APPROVED	10/07/63			-14.0
01-176	ENGINEERING RELEASE	10/21/63			-14.0

FIG. 23. PERT computer readout report—expected date sequence.

Other output reports are available, such as a sort by organizational responsibility, or, as mentioned previously, a sort by events and activities at a particular shred-out level, again depending upon the particular PERT/TIME computer program being used. We shall discuss only the three basic output reports of PERT/TIME, and their use in connection with analysis and replanning.

Analysis and Replanning

The *Slack Order Report* is generally the first concern of the PERT analyst. As seen in Figure 21, it shows all the paths of the network in *order of criticality*—i.e., from largest negative slack, through zero slack, to increasing values of positive slack. At this point the analyst may choose to draw in the critical path and most significant subcritical paths on the actual network in order to study problem areas in a graphical format.

The Event Order Report, Figure 22, is useful at this stage as a cross reference when checking through the network. The *Expected Date Report,* Figure 23, is useful in looking at events and activities in terms of their calendar sequence; it is also useful in developing the final calendar schedule plan.

The PERT analyst now has the option of either preparing a tentative calendar schedule plan, based upon his own replanning carried out under the ground rules stated at the end of Chapter 1, or presenting the basic calculated data at a follow-up PERT meeting. At this point, particularly on large programs, he may wish to run through a number of *simulation exercises* to determine the exact effect on critical-path outcome of changing activity sequences or transferring resources. If a significant amount of negative slack exists on one or more critical paths, it is obvious that a follow-up meeting which has been called for replanning purposes is of the utmost importance. Not only project management but top management as well should attend if there are important decisions to be made in terms of allocating the company's resources and establishing final project goals. The role of the PERT analyst at this point is to make sure that all the basic ground rules for replanning as described in the final pages of Chapter 2 are followed. The final decisions taken during replanning, however, are properly the responsibility of management, not the PERT analyst.

Scheduling

When the basic process of replanning has been accomplished (which may require a number of iterations), the conversion of the network to a final calendar schedule plan is carried out. Calendar scheduling involves consideration of such factors as total manpower loading and availability, funding limitations, vacation periods and holidays, and any special company rules with respect to the use of overtime and double shifts. As mentioned previously, the analyst may have considered special loading factors, to the extent they are significant, in his initial networking. He now sets up a final calendar plan for the program, taking into account the above factors and any other special ones.

Consideration of these factors may affect the decision on where to allocate positive slack, as discussed in Chapter 2. Thus a mechanical approach to final scheduling is generally not possible. In the area of total manpower loading, however, an explicit approach toward obtaining calendar summarization of labor skills is possible. The particular procedure involved will be discussed in connection with PERT/COST in Chapter 4. This approach involves the use of positive slack activities for "leveling" manpower requirements. However, this procedure can only be used on projects which have undergone a complete PERT/COST analysis.

Multiproject Problem

This discussion emphasizes one of the major problems of PERT, namely, that it is project-oriented, and does not explicitly handle the *multiproject problem* for large organizations which are carrying out many projects on a simultaneous basis. It will be recalled, however, that in many such organizations personnel staffing in critical categories is done on *project-structured* basis, and the multiproject problem is not of major significance in this situation. The multiproject problem comes particularly to the fore, however, in such common resource centers as drafting rooms or shops. The solution here, in lieu of the use of the complete PERT/COST procedure, is to assess manpower requirements in terms of conventional loading analysis, using manpower projections from projects which have been PERTed as well as those which have not. After such an "aggregate" loading analysis has been made, priority decisions or assumptions for each project must be established. The result may be that elapsed-time estimates on affected portions of the PERT networks will have to be changed. This is one of the reasons, as we shall see in Chapter 4, that the concept of t_s, a *scheduled elapsed time*, is introduced in place of t_e, the calculated expected time, in the application of PERT/COST.

Finally, it should be pointed out that more refined techniques for handling the multiproject allocation problem have been developed. One of these assumes a cost-time model of the type that will be discussed at the end of Chapter 4.[1] * Another, which has been developed as a complete computer processing routine and which is called RAMPS (Resource Allocation and Multi-Project Scheduling system—CEIR, Inc.), assumes single-activity costing; i.e., it requires manpower skills to be associated with each activity on the network.[2] Finally, there have been studies concerned with multiproject problems from the point of view of probability of receiving a contract award.[3] However, in this book we shall only treat the case where the probability of actually executing the work is assumed to be very high—1.0 or close to it.

Squared Networks

After the completion of the scheduling process, the network may be converted into a calendar or "squared" format, as shown in Figure 24, which is adapted from Figure 6. Here the critical-path length is used to set the calendar scale, and the *residual positive slack* in this simple example is shown with a dashed line. The squared network is a convenient form for displaying the final schedule decisions on any given program. It does have the disadvantage of not being flexible to change at every updating period. The analyst may also wish to prepare at this point a simplified or summary Gantt Chart version of the squared network, particularly for higher management review.

* Superscript numbers indicate items listed in the References at the end of the chapter.

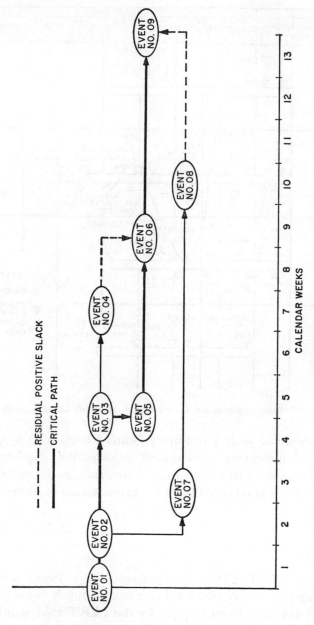

— — — RESIDUAL POSITIVE SLACK

——— CRITICAL PATH

EVENT NO. 01

EVENT NO. 02

EVENT NO. 03

EVENT NO. 04

EVENT NO. 05

EVENT NO. 06

EVENT NO. 07

EVENT NO. 08

EVENT NO. 09

CALENDAR WEEKS

1   2   3   4   5   6   7   8   9   10   11   12   13

Fig. 24. Figure 6 in squared network form.

79

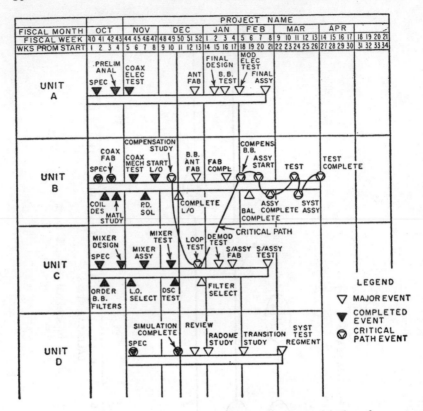

FIG. 25. Sample summary Gantt Chart, showing critical path.

One example of such a summary Gantt Chart, with a special method of indicating critical-path information, is shown in Figure 25.[4] A slack trend summary chart, such as the one shown in Figure 26, is also very helpful for presentation to higher management.[5]

Updating

In most PERT/TIME applications, the network schedule plan is updated every two weeks or every month. This process generally involves direct inquiry by the PERT analyst into the

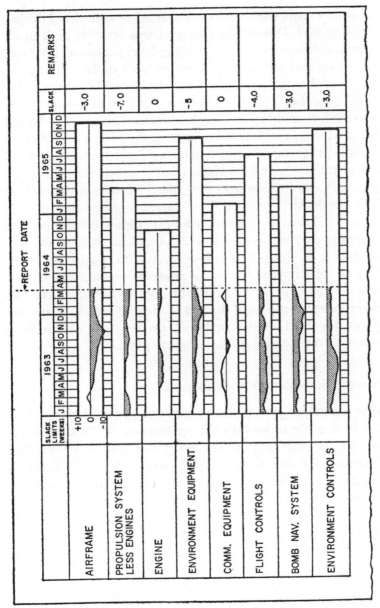

FIG. 26. Slack trend summary.

81

status of all events scheduled to be started or completed during the prior period. During the course of this activity, he is in direct communication with the operating-level personnel involved. His qualities and abilities, in terms of both understanding the substance of the work being performed and making constructive suggestions on how to improve performance, will come particularly to the fore at this point. In this connection, the experienced PERT analyst will wish to participate in the *design review* meetings of the program, in order to have a deeper understanding of technical problems and progress. During the process of updating, he will also inquire into new time estimates for *future activities,* particularly in critical-path areas or when new trouble spots are indicated by accumulated experience on the project.

Updating does not generally involve all activities of the network, but it is likely to produce new critical-path and slack data. Thus the formal process of analysis, replanning, and review is started over again, and continues to recycle every two weeks or every month until the end of the program. The amount of effort involved in the updating process will clearly be a function of the quality of the original plan.

Network Condensation and Integration

After a network plan has been converted to a calendar schedule, it is possible to go into the application of PERT/COST. Before treating this subject, however, we shall examine one final and particularly significant aspect of the PERT/TIME, which represents a unique contribution of the technique, namely, *network condensation and integration.*

In large defense and space programs it is typical for there to be many different networks, since many companies throughout the country are working on the same program. One objective of the top manager of such a program, whether it be a prime contractor or a government agency, is to achieve a *valid summarization* of all these different networks. The problem involves identification of all the interface events common to two or more networks, and the ability to determine T_E's and critical-path analysis for the *totality of all networks*. It should be realized that the total of all networks may amount to more than 30,000 activities on large programs. The process by which this summarization is achieved is known as network *condensation, integration, and validation,* and is shown in Figures 27 to 29.[6]

First, key events on the detailed network of any given con-

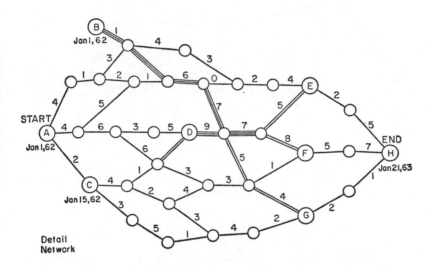

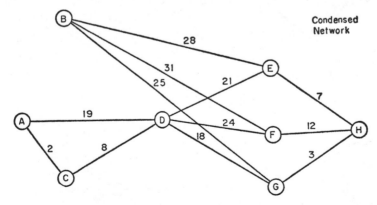

Fig. 27. Network condensation.

tractor are selected, as shown in the top portion of Figure 27. This will include starting and terminating events, important milestone events, and all interface events with other networks. Next the computer calculates all possible paths between any pair of these events, and selects the longest path in the case of each pair. The result is a *condensed or skeletonized* network,

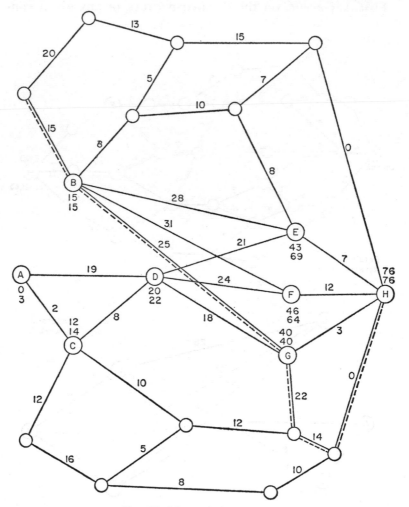

FIG. 28. Network integration.

as shown in the lower half of Figure 27. The activity lines connecting the events of the condensed network shown in Figure 27 do not have any significance in terms of usual activity definition, but represent a valid T_E calculation between any two selected events. During the condensation process the number of network activities may be reduced by a factor of 10 to 1.

The next step is that all the condensed networks on a given program are tied together or integrated through their interface events. An example of an interface event is Event B in Figure

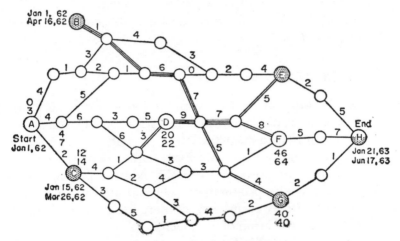

FIG. 29. Network validation.

28. A new T_E and critical-path calculation is then made through the integrated network. The results of such a calculation often produce a different T_E outlook for the terminating event of the original detailed network as compared to the first T_E calculation for that network. This is because of the impact of time constraints coming in from other networks through the interface event. As an example, the new T_E outlook of the terminating event of the detailed network is changed by six months, as shown in Figure 29. Because of this effect of integration, all T_E's on the original detailed network must now be recalculated, a process known as *validation*.

It should be realized that, by means of network condensation and integration, and, sometimes, recondensation, an entire national program can be viewed in one final, comprehensible summarized network. Though the activity lines of such a network have, in general, no identifiable meaning, the calculated expected times are valid, as derived from the underlying detailed network system. This process represents a contribution unique to the PERT technique; indeed it would be hard to visualize how it could be accomplished with any other schedule reporting system. It is an example of the power of the PERT technique as an important new tool for management of large, complex programs.

Use of PERT/TIME in Production

The applicability of PERT to production operations is a subject of continuing discussion and investigation. The fact that PERT is not useful in such situations as continuous assembly-line production appears obvious. Even here, however, one must be careful to distinguish between the flow or process charts used in planning the production cycle and a PERT network. Though the two may seem very similar, the former system is used for the determination of such factors as cycle times and line balancing, while the PERT technique, at least as it is generally defined, is oriented toward critical-path analysis of a one-time-through project.

It is also important to emphasize that there are areas of production where PERT planning and control techniques are very much applicable. One area involves the preliminary manufacturing phases of production protoype or pilot model construction and the buildup of tooling and facilities for large-scale production. Still another area involves the actual fabrication, assembly, and test of initial production units, generally of a large, complex nature, which are still "high on the learning curve." Individual networks for these phases of production can often be quite useful; after these phases, established production control techniques are generally more applicable.

It should be noted, however, that many of the complex defense and space programs never leave these preliminary production phases, or at least never enter into mass production. As was mentioned in Chapter 1, the current trend for many programs of a limited-production character is to integrate the techniques of PERT with established control methods such as line of balance or similar techniques which bring in the quantity factor. One example of this is the PERT/LOB system described in Army Materiel Command Regulation 11–16 on Planning and Control Techniques for Project Management.[7]

In this same area of large, complex programs, the PERT technique is often used in the form of master networking of an entire systems acquisition program. In this case, aggregate or summary level activities are shown for the production of a given lot or series of equipments, and the delivery of these equipments to other organizations for integration or testing purposes is shown in network form.

Other Uses—Long-range Planning

Just as PERT can be applied with a certain flexibility of approach to the production phase, so can it be applied to the early conceptual or feasibility investigation stages of a program. Thus it is possible to use the network approach in the early stages of long-range planning or in initial efforts leading up to the formal definition of a program. However, this type of application rarely contains much critical-path significance, since the end goals of this early planning effort have not been, or cannot be, clearly defined. In this situation interim goals may be established, such as a "Go-No-Go" decision for a commercial new-product venture, after preliminary marketing investigations have been completed. In long-range applications of this kind, there may be a series of networks, each terminating in a Go-No-Go ending event. Early planning networks of this type usually represent the dependency relationships between the various elements of the organization which must participate in initial planning and conceptual efforts. The network can be "calendar-time-scheduled" or not, depending on the urgency which is believed to exist concerning completion of the early planning effort.

One further use of PERT/TIME, which is closely related to these early planning applications, is the development of *administrative networks*. These are networks showing the relationship between administrative activities and key management decisions or action points. In the complex activities of the government such networks have been widely used; there is no reason why they could not be comparably used in private industry. Included in the concept of administrative networks are such actions as effecting a reorganization or planning a merger. Here again, there may or may not be much critical-path significance, and the network will generally be calendar-time-scaled. With this range of applicability, it should be obvious that exact criteria for the use of PERT are difficult to state. PERT can be used effectively on small programs as well as large ones; perhaps the main criterion for its use is that there should be some degree of complexity or interrelationship involved in the effort being PERTed.

REFERENCES

1. A. A. McGee and M. D. Markarian, "Optimum Allocation of Research/ Engineering Manpower Within a Multi-Project Organizational Structure," *IRE Transactions on Engineering Management*, vol. EM-9, no. 3, pp. 104–108, September, 1962.
2. *RAMPS Training Text and User's Guide*, CEIR, Inc., New York, 1962.
3. K. S. Packard, "Probabilistic Forecasting of Manpower Requirements," *IRE Transactions on Engineering Management*, vol. EM-9, no. 3, pp. 136–138, September, 1962.
4. Jerome Pearlman, "Engineering Program Planning and Control through the Use of PERT," *IRE Transactions on Engineering Management*, vol. 7, p. 128, 1960.
5. *Air Force Systems Command PERT/TIME System Description Manual*, p. 61, June, 1963.
6. *Ibid.*, pp. 198–201.
7. AMCR 11–16, "Planning and Control Techniques for Project Management," vol II. pp. 4.1–4.64, August, 1963.

4

PERT/COST

Introduction

In the first portion of this book we covered the need for a new
program management system and, in response to that need, the
methodology and implementation problems of the PERT/
TIME technique. We now turn to one of the most important developments in PERT Management Systems, namely, the introduction of costs in an explicit relationship with the network,
or PERT/COST.

It will be remembered that the original Navy research team
recognized that the network might provide an ideal framework
for the development of costs on complex programs. However,
they wisely decided to forego the treatment of costs because of
the initial difficulties of implementing PERT/TIME. The
problems of implementing PERT/COST are equally great,
although somewhat different in character.

At the outset it should be clear that PERT/COST cannot
be considered independently of PERT/TIME; in fact, the term
PERT/COST includes the assumption that networks must be

89

fully developed before the costing phase can be completed. As we shall see, the persons involved in the costing phase must have an intimate knowledge of the network. Indeed, to be really effective, they should be the same persons who were involved in establishing the configuration and estimating times for activities on the original network. In addition, it is doubtful that any organization can successfully implement PERT/COST unless it has had considerable experience in the problems of implementing PERT/TIME. All these requirements are consistent with the central idea of PERT/COST, which is the direct coupling, or association, of program costs with activities on an established time network. It is perhaps worth emphasizing again that in the use of PERT/COST we are concerned with one-time-through programs, and not repetitive manufacturing situations where costs are associated with the number of units produced.

Objectives of PERT/COST

The basic objectives of PERT/COST are twofold: (1) to achieve a significantly better, or more realistic, original program cost estimate; and (2) once the program is authorized to proceed, to achieve a marked improvement in control against the original estimate.

The significance of these objectives can perhaps better be appreciated by reference to Table 7. Let us suppose a high govern-

TABLE 7. ORIGINAL ESTIMATES VERSUS FINAL COST FOR A NUMBER OF PROGRAMS

	Before PERT/COST	After PERT/COST
Original estimates	$100 million	$150 million
Final actual costs	$200 million	$165 million
Cost factor increase	2.0	1.1

ment official or industry executive is responsible for approving programs based upon original estimates of $100 million, as shown in the first column of Table 7. As we have seen, for the **various** reasons outlined in Chapter 1, actual costs for such programs can easily increase to twice the original estimates. If the executive approves all the programs based upon the original estimates, he will later have to seek additional funds, possibly by not authorizing the start-up of future programs, which have a priority as high as any of those in the originally authorized group. Alternatively, he may have to terminate some of the programs already in progress, if he is constrained by an overall budgetary or resource limitation. In either case, there is serious impact on the program planning and approval process, as well as a large amount of waste and loss for both the industry and the nation. (It will be recalled from Chapter 1 that fifty-seven national defense programs were canceled during the ten-year period from 1953 to 1963, representing an investment of $6.2 billion.)

Suppose the group of programs in Table 7 were estimated more realistically, using PERT/COST techniques. In this case, the cost estimates would probably be higher, or $150 million, as shown in column 2 of Table 7. By implication, if the executive were under a condition of budgetary or resource constraint, he would not approve the lower-priority projects, because these estimates would show he could not afford it. After approval of the higher-priority projects, he would hope to obtain a greatly improved degree of control against original estimates for these projects. As shown in column 2 of Table 7, the result might be a maximum of a 10 per cent increase over original estimates, rather than a 100 per cent increase. On this basis, all the high-priority projects originally approved could probably be carried through to completion.

These, then, are the principle objectives of PERT/COST, in addition to cost reduction. There are potential areas of cost reduction or increase in efficiency made possible by the proper application of PERT Management Systems; these have been discussed in Chapter 3, and specific illustrations are given in Chapter 6. By and large, however, these latter gains, some of which are difficult to cost out exactly, may not be as significant as the gains to be achieved in original decision making at the program approval stage and improved control during the execution of approved programs.

It may well be asked how such improved project cost control is actually achieved with PERT/COST, particularly in view of the history of cost escalation on complex programs described in Chapter 1. Figure 30 illustrates the cost planning and con-

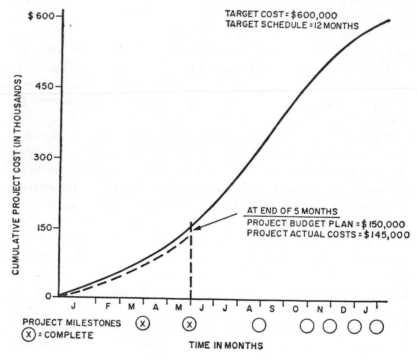

FIG. 30. Conventional project cost control approach.

trol approach classically used in most organizations. Until the advent of PERT/COST, it was also widely used for the planning and control of project work. The solid line in Figure 30 represents the cumulative budget or plan for the project on a calendar scale. It will be noted that two milestones, originally scheduled for the first five months of the program, are shown as being complete. Since actual costs are shown to be slightly under plan, and two scheduled milestones have been completed, this program would appear to be in excellent control.

Actually, the program is already in serious trouble. The reasons why it is in trouble can best be explained by reference to Figure 31. Here we see that the first five months of the program

	PROJECT STATUS AS OF MAY 31		
	BUDGET	ACTUAL	OVER (+) UNDER (−)
TASK 1	$25	$25	$0 (TASK COMPLETED MARCH 31)
TASK 2	35	70	+35 (TASK COMPLETED MAY 31)
TASK 3	40	20	−20
TASK 4	35	20	−15
TASK 5	15	10	−5
TOTAL	$150	$145	$−5

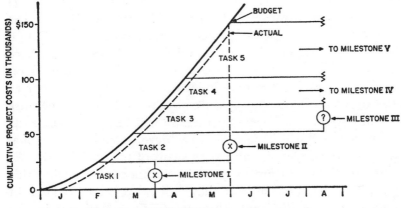

Fig. 31. PERT/COST control approach.

were actually composed of five separate tasks. Each of these tasks has its own individual time and cost projections, which should be viewed horizontally, as shown in Figure 31. It will be noted that Task 1 was completed on its budget of $25,000, and its terminating milestone was also achieved. Task 2, however, expended $70,000 against an originally planned budget of $35,000, to achieve its milestone event. Tasks 3, 4, and 5 underexpended their budgets by the amounts indicated in Figure

31. This probably happened because these tasks did not get started up in accordance with the planned schedule. The combination of underexpenditures on Tasks 3, 4, and 5 offset the overexpenditure on Task 2. The net effect appears to be an excellent expenditure picture if the aggregate planning and control approach shown in Figure 30 is used. Actually, as we can see, the program already has a built-in $35,000 overrun within the first five months of effort. The potential overrun may be even higher than this if we attempt to maintain schedule on the downstream milestones of Tasks 3, 4, and 5, since this may involve putting some crash effort into these tasks, particularly Task 3, at this point. Thus, Figure 31 indicates that, rather than an excellent time and cost outlook, we really have a program which has a minimum built-in overrun of $35,000, and which is currently in schedule jeopardy.

The above illustration demonstrates the purpose of using the PERT/COST approach to project control. With PERT/COST the program manager is clearly under no illusions as to where he stands. He will be forced to make some hard decisions on how he will modify the remainder of the program in order to meet overall cost and/or schedule objectives. However, because he will have had sufficient warning, he will be able to made decisions that will still be possible to achieve. It should be emphasized that the dollar size and time spans of the individual tasks shown in Figure 31 are of great importance in achieving this improved degree of control; they will be referred to later in connection with the establishment of *Work Packages* in the PERT/COST system.

Background of PERT/COST

We now turn to the background of what is often called basic PERT/COST, or DOD (Department of Defense) PERT/COST, since the requirements of the basic PERT/COST system adopted by the Federal government were first officially set

forth in a document entitled *DOD/NASA PERT/COST Guide,*
dated June, 1962.[1] * The consultant on the development of
DOD PERT/COST was Management Systems, Inc., of Cambridge, Massachusetts, headed by J. Sterling Livingston of the
Harvard Business School. It will be recalled from Chapter 2
that, after the introduction of PERT/TIME in 1958, there was
a rapid multiplication of PERT-oriented program management
systems throughout the country, particularly in those companies engaged in defense and space work. A representative list-
ing of such systems is given in Appendix 3. During the period
from 1959 to 1962 many of these systems brought in the cost
factor in one way or another. For example, a system such as
IBM's LESS (Least-cost Estimating and Scheduling System),
which is the computerized version of the original CPM costing
approach, represents a special type of time and cost model to
be discussed at the end of this chapter.

The issuance of the *DOD/NASA Guide* of 1962, and its per-
sonal endorsement by both Secretary of Defense R. S. Mc-
Namara and Associate Administrator R. C. Seamans, Jr. of
NASA, tended to bring about a high degree of uniformity in
the approach to basic PERT/COST. Indeed, after its issuance,
many companies began dropping their privately developed
PERT/COST systems.

Another significant facet of development of PERT/COST is
the unified approach which has been achieved by the various
agencies of the Federal government. Figure 32 shows the high
organization level and degree of participation by Federal government agencies in this field. It will be noted that under the
Assistant Secretary of Defense for Logistics and Material, who
reports to the Secretary of Defense, there is an interagency Task
Force on Industrial Management Practices. This task force has
representatives from the Department of Defense (including
Army, Navy, and Air Force), NASA (National Aeronautics and

* Superscript numbers indicate items listed in the References at the end of the
chapter.

Space Administration), Atomic Energy Commission, Federal Aviation Authority, Bureau of the Budget, and other Federal agencies.

Under this group there is a PERT Coordinating Committee, which has exercised very strong control over the development

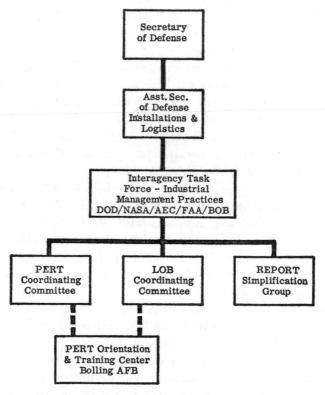

Fig. 32. DOD PERT Coordinating Committee.

of a uniform PERT/COST system for the Federal government. An example of this control is the fact that the exact formats of the output reports of the basic PERT/COST system were agreed to in early 1963 by all participating agencies. These were then issued as Supplement No. 1 to the original *DOD/NASA PERT/COST Guide.* This kind of agreement on a *new* management system represents a remarkable accomplishment, and there is probably no precedent for it in the history of United States economic and industrial development. It should be pointed out that this uniform approach benefits industry, or at least industry involved in government contract work, to the extent that individual agencies do not have different reporting requirements. As was mentioned in Chapter 1 and will be noted in Figure 32, a group similar to the PERT Coordinating Committee has been established on line-of-balance production control methods.

Basic PERT/COST

We shall now cover the methodology of basic PERT/COST, with emphasis on the specific requirements of the system as established by the Department of Defense and agencies represented on the PERT/COST Coordinating Committee.

One of the first differences between PERT/TIME and PERT/COST, from the point of view of the analyst, is that in the PERT/COST application the networking of the program must be very complete. Generally speaking, all activities which generate a direct cost to the program must be indicated on the network, or tied to the Work Breakdown Structure through a Work Package. This is a very different approach than in earlier applications of PERT/TIME, where only major elements of the program thought to have an effect on schedule outcome were generally PERTed. It is clear that if we wish to develop the cost of a program in association with networks, we would like to talk about the *total cost of the program,* and not a figure with some unknown percentage of the program costs missing.

This requirement may lead to creating activities on the network which do not appear to have too much PERT significance. Thus, if *program management* is considered a direct charge, an activity line can be established for it over the length of the program, as a minimum networking approach. Though there is often objection to such an approach in PERT/COST, it is a curious fact that the relationship between cost and time in the case of program management is one of the most significant, or highly correlated. Thus, if the predicted completion time of a program should extend by two months, program management costs are almost certain to increase linearly by a corresponding amount.

Work Breakdown Structure

In order to provide a framework for *complete networking,* the Work Breakdown Structure discussed in Chapter 3 was formally introduced as the first item of analysis in carrying out basic PERT/COST. It will be recalled that the Work Breakdown Structure, as illustrated in Figure 18 in Chapter 3, is product-oriented in character. Thus, its End Item Subdivisions are consistent with the way networks are developed in most PERT/TIME applications. Figure 33 is an illustration of a Work Breakdown Structure for a larger program, taken from the *DOD/NASA Guide.*

In connection with larger programs, such as the one illustrated in Figure 33, there has been considerable controversy on the subject of at what level the Work Breakdown Structure should become "functionally," i.e., organizationally, structured versus "product-structured." Suffice it to say that one of the main objectives of PERT/COST, and in fact one of its new features, is to establish a time and cost correlation for *tasks,* which are a product-oriented phenomenon. As will be seen, functionally oriented budget and cost information is available from the PERT/COST system, but as a derivative, and not as a prime feature. It should be pointed out that portions of the Work Breakdown Structure can be structured on a functional basis, where task orientation is not significant, such as in the case of program management or systems engineering.

It should be remembered, however, that the Work Breakdown Structure does not usually correspond on a one-to-one basis with the organization structure. For a given program, this relationship must generally be established by a Task Matrix of the type discussed in Chapter 3, Figure 19. With flexibility in approach, the Work Breakdown Structure can also be developed to handle items which do not fit neatly into the product-oriented End Item Subdivision category. Examples of these items are documentation, which represents a very significant part of the costs of large weapons programs, and system integration and testing.

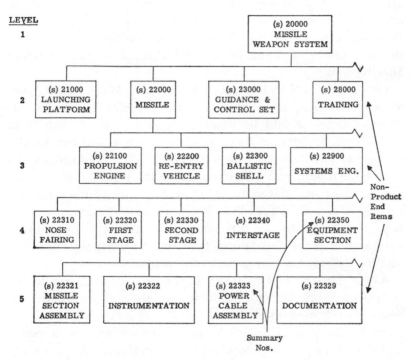

Fɪɢ. 33. Illustration of Work Breakdown from *DOD PERT/COST Guide.*

Though the most significant feature of the Work Breakdown Structure is to provide a framework for identifying all the major tasks of a program—with particular emphasis on product-oriented structuring of these tasks—very little is said in the *DOD/NASA Guide* about at what point in the life of a program a meaningful Work Breakdown Structure can be established, and to what degree the content or substance of the tasks within it is defined. The importance of the stability of the

Work Breakdown Structure and its relationship to systems engineering have been mentioned previously, and will be extensively discussed in Chapter 5. Here it will be emphasized that the Work Breakdown Structure provides the vital framework for coupling program *performance factors* with *time and cost factors*. If properly developed, it provides the key to an integrated program management system for performance, time, and cost factors. If there are any areas of the initial Work Breakdown Structure which are not thoroughly developed and defined, provision must be made for *contingency* End Item Subdivisions.

One other problem connected with the Work Breakdown Structure is that, in carrying out work under a contract, all contract items should be made at least consistent with it at some level. Otherwise there will be much confusion in the estimating and reporting of costs, and double bookkeeping in both government and industry may be the result. For this reason, contract negotiators must be made aware of the basic approach to the PERT/COST Work Breakdown Structure for any given program. In this same area, it should be pointed out that the Work Breakdown Structure may have to be modified for different major phases of a program.

As can be seen in Figure 33, it is generally necessary to develop the Work Breakdown Structure through a number of levels, i.e., five or more levels on a major development program, before an End Item level is reached against which meaningful PERT/TIME networks can be developed. After a thorough PERT/TIME analysis has been carried out covering all the End Item Subdivisions, including such final network areas as system integration and test, the next step is to establish *Cost Work Packages* which are associated with the networks.

Cost Work Packages

With established networks in front of him, the analyst is ready to undertake the extension into basic PERT/COST

Work Packages. In the controversy that inevitably surrounds a new management system there are some who feel that you must have been doing PERT/COST all the time while you are carrying out a PERT/TIME analysis. There is a certain amount of truth in this position as regards assumptions on available or planned level of resources when estimating elapsed times for a given network activity. But there is a great deal of difference between being *explicit vs. implicit* about such cost elements as number of man-hours, types of skills, outside material dollars, etc., involved in establishing a network activity time estimate. There is also the problem of costing individual versus groups of activities, since, on a typical valid operating PERT network, far more detail is involved than is found in most industrial job order structures.

The DOD approach to PERT/COST resolved this as the problem of "single-versus-multiple-activity" costing. Clearly, if a job cost account were to be established for each activity on a detailed PERT network, the number of job accounts and amount of reporting detail would increase by an order of magnitude in most industrial accounting systems. The approach used in basic PERT/COST is to aggregate a group of activities within the network into a *Cost Work Package*. Figure 34 illustrates the establishment of two Work Packages against a portion of a detailed network. It should be pointed out that all activities in the network under an End Item Subdivision must fall within a Work Package, and that all Work Packages must be capable of summarization to an End Item Subdivision.

The precise criteria by which the PERT analyst goes about establishing a Work Package are not given in the *DOD/NASA Guide,* and the job is more difficult than might be realized. One criterion given in the *DOD/NASA Guide* is that Work Packages should be of the general magnitude of three months' duration, and another is that Work Packages should not exceed $100,000 in cost. We have seen previously, in Figure 31, why the three-month ground rule might be a meaningful criterion for establishing the majority of the Work Packages on a PERT network, if horizontal task planning and control are emphasized over vertical calendar cost control. It should be emphasized, however, that this figure is only a guide. The range of time spans for Work Packages might be from one to six months, with special cases taking a year or more, such as program management.

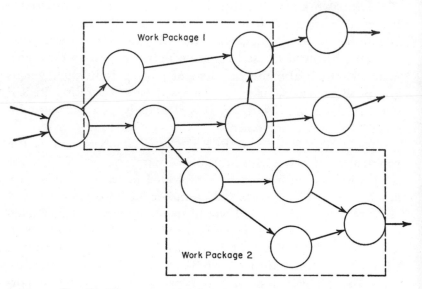

FIG. 34. Illustration of Work Packages against network.

If Work Packages are set up on the basis of the three-month ground rule, their dollar size is often predetermined, depending on the particular program or industry. For example, in the electronics industry, a typical three-month Work Package in the development portion of the network might range in dollar size from $10,000 to $50,000. The actual dollar size of a Work Package depends upon many factors; some of these are listed below:

1. *Industry involved.* For example, electronics versus aircraft, with their individual problems and control practices.

2. *Stage of program.* For example, early development phase vs. fabrication, testing, and redesign phase. At the prototype fabrication stage, Work Packages will tend to have a higher dollar value because of a higher material content. In addition, it is generally necessary to set up longer Work Packages at the redesign phase, when many small engineering changes are being made, as compared to the early development phase.

3. *Size of program.* Usually a small program with a short time schedule will have smaller and shorter Work Packages then a large program. It is not at all obvious, however, that Work Package sizes should increase proportionally with the size of program. The offsetting factor here is the *intrinsic* size of the job for planning and control purposes at the level of operating supervision.

4. *Depth and shape of Work Breakdown Structure.* If the Work Breakdown Structure goes to a low level and has a wide horizontal base (as is common in the electronics industry), Work Packages will tend to be smaller in size.

There are other factors that are important in the difficult job of establishing Work Packages. These have to do with achieving improved benefits in internal control; there will often be differences of viewpoint in this area *within* an industry or even within an organization. The intrinsic size of the job, as seen by the operating-level supervisor, has already been referred to. If general management or the financial organization does not feel it is worth reporting costs to this level, and at the same time places heavy pressure on operating supervisors to meet budgets, "bootleg accounting" may be the result. This problem exists whether or not PERT/COST is involved; however, in implementing PERT/COST, care must be exercised to examine the Work Order system already in existence and to see how it is meeting organizational requirements. In the shop area, Work Orders may be very detailed, and therefore may have to be treated as a further breakdown of the Work Package;

in the development and engineering area, Work Orders may be too large for effective control, and may have to be broken down into finer-grained Work Packages.

Another problem which the analyst must face in order to get the maximum benefit out of correlating time and cost performance in the PERT/COST system is that of establishing *clear starting and terminating events* for each Work Package. In order to get maximum "coupling" benefit, Work Packages must be built around continuous paths, as shown in Figure 34. Another problem is whether the Work Package is purely functional, or whether it can represent another level of task breakdown involving several organization elements and/or resource skills. The criteria for Work Package continuity can at times be at variance with the criteria for a single-function Work Package. In this connection, many organizations have already established procedures identifying functions and labor skills in their present cost reporting systems. This allows the PERT/COST analyst greater flexibility in establishing Work Packages.

All the above constraints and factors will have to be taken into account by the PERT/COST analyst in setting up a Work Package structure which is meaningful and useful. As has been previously indicated, a considerable amount of judgment is involved, in addition to a depth of knowledge on the content of the network. A final point is that a single person or party in the organization should be indicated as having "unit responsibility" for any one Work Package.

Inputs and Outputs

With the development of the Work Breakdown Structure and time networks, followed by the establishment of Work Packages (including cost estimates) against the time networks, the initial steps of PERT/COST implementation have been completed. Work Package cost estimating data are typically developed on the type of format shown in Figure 35; here man-hour requirements by resource skills, either in "prime form"

	PROGRAM	CONTRACTOR	CONTRACT NO.	NETWORK CODE	RESPONSIBLE ORGN.
	MWS	XYZ	ABC-123	1A	2217

SUMMARY NO: 816555	DESCRIPTION: SERVO PLATFORM	AS OF DATE: 31 NOV 61
CHARGE NO: 71834031	DESCRIPTION: SERVO PLATFORM DESIGN	REPORT DATE: 9 DEC 61

EVENT NO.

	EARLIEST DATE	SCHEDULED DATE
Beginning: 12345678 (First)	Start Date: 20 MAR 62	Start Date: 20 mar'62
Ending: 12348765 (Last)	End Date: 30 AUG 62	End Date: 30 aug'62

RESOURCE ESTIMATES

MONTHS BEGINNING WITH SCHEDULED START DATE

IDENTIFICATION U D C	Perf. Orgn.	Res. Code	1 MAR	2 APR	3 MAY	4 JUN	5 JUL	6 AUG	7 SEP	8 OCT	9 NOV	10 DEC	11 JAN	12 FEB	TOTAL
H	5416	62	1700	3200	4300	1900									
H	5416	93		2300	2600		1700								
D	4816	10		46000	50000										
D	9616	22		16000	13000	15000	9000	1700							

Estimator: ~~R.W.~~

Approved by: a.F.B.

Date: 15 Dec 61

Fig. 35. PERT/COST Estimating and Updating Form.

105

or converted to dollars, together with material dollars are estimated for input into the PERT/COST system. It is important to point out that the time data on Figure 35 are based upon *scheduled elapsed times*, or t_s, for network activities, which may, for scheduling reasons, be different from the expected time figure t_e. Another important point to emphasize in connection with Figure 35 is that in some PERT/COST computer programs this basic input form is reproduced as an output, showing latest actual and original budget data. This form can then be transmitted directly to personnel responsible for reestimating, which greatly speeds up the updating process.

Generally speaking, some sort of data-processing equipment is required for the handling of PERT/COST, just as it is for any detailed cost accounting system. A minimum data-processing equipment configuration may be sufficient; but to produce the full spectrum of DOD PERT/COST outputs on a computer basis, a medium- to large-scale machine is usually required. Figure 35 shows the most significant computer input that is required; other input information (such as rate tables) may be required, depending on the particular PERT/COST computer program being used.

There are a number of outputs from the DOD PERT/COST system; as mentioned previously, these have been agreed upon by all Federal government agencies concerned and issued as Supplement No. 1 to the *DOD/NASA Guide.*[2] A brief description is given below of the most significant features of each of these output reports. It should be emphasized again that the general policy of the government is to require only top-level reports such as the Management Summary Report. The question of what level of the Work Breakdown Structure will be called for in the Management Summary Report has been a subject of controversy. Generally speaking, for a large system such as the one shown in Figure 33, levels 2 and 3 of the Work Breakdown Structure are called for. Such a policy on the part of the government is based upon the assumption that a contractor has established a complete PERT/COST system, and is properly maintaining the underlying data which feed into these top-level reports.

1. *Management Summary Report* (Figure 36). This is the top program-management-oriented report of the basic PERT/COST system. It typically covers a *subsystem,* or second-level item on the Work Breakdown Structure, and all the third-level items underneath the subsystem. Costs are displayed on a "Work Performed to Date" and "Totals at Completion" basis. It should be noted that under the "Work Performed to Date" heading, the first column is labeled "Value," meaning *value of work performed.* This is *not* the original planned budget through the current calendar date, but, rather, represents a special computation relating to the planned budgets of all completed Work Packages and those which are still in process. The figure in the Value column is obtained by adding the originally planned budgets for all completed Work Packages and the planned budgets for all Work Packages in process, multiplied by the ratio of Actual-to-Date to Revised-Forecast-at-Completion for each of these Work Packages in process. The accuracy of this calculation is therefore a function of the length of Work Packages; the shorter the Work Package, generally speaking, the greater the accuracy of forecast at completion. The purpose of the value figure is to provide a consistent basis for comparing budget to actual in the case of Work Packages which have actually had effort expended on them. Its introduction assumes there may be Work Packages which were not started in accordance with the original schedule plan owing to the changes in network schedules at the detailed level. This concept requires a complete explanation for personnel who will be using it. Most program managers are accustomed to seeing cumulative budgets based upon the original plan; this figure, and comparison to actual, is not given until the Financial Plan and Status Report. There are other approaches to establishing a figure which relates actual costs to budgets for the work "actually undertaken." The term *value* as used here may be somewhat misleading; perhaps the term *Earned Budget* would be clearer.

108

ABC - MISSILE AND GHE		REPORTING ORGN.	CONTRACT NO.	REPORT DATES	
LEVEL/SUMMARY ITEM: 1/BALLISTIC SHELL 22300		XYZ - A&S DIVN 22300	33(600)28369A	TERM (SPAN): TOTAL PROGRAM / CUT OFF DATE: 30MAR63 / RELEASE DATE: 10APR63	

COST OF WORK $(000)

ITEM	WORK PERFORMED TO DATE			TOTALS AT COMPLETION			MOST CRIT SLACK (WKS)	COMPL DATE	SCHEDULE	REMARKS
	VALUE	ACTUAL COST	(OVERRUN) UNDERRUN	PLANNED COST	LATEST REVISED EST	PROJECTED (OVERRUN) UNDERRUN				
BALLISTIC SHELL LEV 3 22300	19,600	20,500	(900) (.05)	35,200	39,650	(4,450) (.13)	0.0	10DEC64 / 31DEC63		SEE PROBLEM ANALYSIS RPT ITEMS 1-3
NOSE FAIRING LEV 4 22310	27	25	2 (.07)	175	175		8.6	10DEC64 / 10JUN63 / 10AUG63		ITEM 6
FIRST STAGE LEV 4 22320	6,700	6,400	300 (.04)	9,200	9,700	(500) (.05)	0.0	30APR64 / 31DEC63 / 31DEC63		ITEMS 9-12
SECOND STAGE LEV 4 22330	1,645	1,650	(5)	3,500	3,570	(70) (.02)	0.0	15JUN64 / 31DEC63 / 31DEC63		ITEM 15

SCHEDULE
S - SCHED COMPL DATE -- TOTAL
A - ACTUAL COMPL DATE -- ITEM
E - EARLIEST COMPL DATE -- CRITICAL
L - LATEST COMPL DATE -- ITEM

P   1963   1964
YRJFMAMJJASONDJFMAMJJASOND

TIME NOW

FIG. 36. PERT/COST Management Summary Report.

On the right-hand side of the Management Summary Report we see schedule data on a comparable basis to cost data, which of course fulfills one of the main objectives of the PERT/COST system. These schedule data are shown on a reduced calendar-time scale, with two columns devoted to a prior year, the next twenty-four columns to two years by months, and the last four columns representing a single year each.

Special attention should be paid to the meaning of the schedule nomenclature in this part of the Management Summary Report. It will be recalled from previous discussion that, at the stage where a network is converted into a calendar schedule plan, we introduce the concept of t_s, the scheduled elapsed time, which may be different than t_e, the calculated expected time. The E shown on the Management Summary Report now represents S_E, the *earliest completion time,* which is very similar to T_E, except that it is the sum of the individual activity t_s's, rather than t_e's. The L shown on the report represents S_L, the *latest completion date,* which is calculated on a comparable basis to T_L, again using t_s's instead of t_e's. The E and the L are shown in connection with the most critical (for instance, highest negative slack) events within the summary item. Thus E and L *may not be directly related* to the scheduled completion date of the last event within the item, which is shown as the S date. This situation would of course be true if there were an interface event with the network of another summary item, and the interface event connected to a path of higher program criticality on the network for the other summary item. The actual date, shown as A, is, however, related to end schedule date S of the summary item.

2. *Program/Project Status Report* (Figure 37). This is similar to the Management Summary Report, except that it goes down to the Work Package level, and shows schedule data in terms of figures under the column labeled "Time Status," rather than on a calendar-time scale. The Program/Project Status Report is intended for use by the industrial program manager or the planning and control personnel within his office.

	REPORTING ORGN.	CONTRACT NO.	REPORT DATES	
ABC – MISSILE AND GHE	XYZ – A&S DIVN	33(600)28369A	TERM (SPAN): TOTAL PROGRAM	
LEVEL/SUMMARY ITEM: 4/FIRST STAGE 22320			CUT OFF DATE: 30MAR63	RELEASE DATE: 10APR63

IDENTIFICATION				TIME STATUS			COST OF WORK $(000)					
							WORK PERFORMED TO DATE			TOTALS AT COMPLETION		
CHARGE OR SUMMARY NUMBER	LEVEL	FIRST EVENT NO.	LAST EVENT NO.	SCHED OR ACT (A) COMPL DATE	EARLIEST & LATEST COMPL DATE	MOST CRIT SLACK (WKS)	VALUE	ACTUAL COST	(OVERRUN) UNDERRUN	PLANNED COST	LATEST REVISED ESTIMA	PROJECTED (OVERRUN) UNDERRUN
FIRST STAGE 22320	4	12000999	12000199	30APR64	31DEC63 31DEC63	0.0 12000612	6,700	6,400	.04 300	9,200	9,700	(.05) (500)
INSTRUMENTATION 22322	5	12000700	12000400	10JAN64	31DEC63 31DEC63	0.0 12000612	165	172	(.04) (7)	415	430	(.04) (15)
POWER CABLE ASSY. 22323	5	12000899	12000800	15FEB64	15JUN63 15JUN63	0.0 12000783	270	200	.26 70	1,250	1,180	.06 70
ELECTRICAL DESIGN 32164	6	12000700	12000420	25JUL63	10JUN63 25JUN63	2.1 12000682	110	112	(.02) (2)	205	209	(.02) (4)
ELECTRICAL DESIGN 32165	6	12000869	12000860	12JAN64	15JUN63 15JUN63	0.0 12000783	22	20	.10 2	175	175	.10 2
MANUFACTURING 52073	6	12000690	12000410	22AUG63	10JUN63 25JUN63	2.1 12000682	55	60	(.11) (5)	125	137	(.10) (12)
TESTING 78340	6	12000622	12000400	10JAN64	31DEC63 31DEC63	0.0 12000612			.01	85	84	.01

Fig. 37. PERT/COST Program/Project Status Report.

3. *Organization Status Report* (Figure 38). The Organization Status Report is directed toward the functionally oriented or department manager, and shows both man-hours and dollar costs associated with Work Packages for which his organization is responsible. Although the term Direct Costs is shown in Figure 38, this figure can include applied overhead if it represents the normal practice of the contractor.

4. *Financial Plan and Status Report* (Figure 39). The Financial Plan and Status Report is directed toward the financial manager or controller, as well as the program manager, and contains data on incremental costs (or costs for the month indicated) and cumulative-to-date planned versus actual costs. This is the first of the regular PERT/COST output reports on which the original cumulative calendar plan or budget is shown. One omission from this report is funding information, i.e., restrictions on expenditures which may be different from planned costs.

5. *Manpower Loading Report* (Figure 40). The Manpower Loading Report is directed toward revealing critical manpower loading situations. The basic problem is shown graphically in Figure 41. Here a calendar summary of total program manpower requirements is shown by particular skill category based upon initial PERT/COST estimates. The peaks and valleys shown are obviously undesirable, along with the fact that peak requirements may exceed manpower availability. The analysis of where leveling can best be achieved is based upon review of the Manpower Loading Report, Figure 40, which shows data on Work Package activities with positive slack. If significant corrections are indicated, a thorough replanning effort, including readjustment of Work Package schedules as well as individual activity t_s figures, may be necessary. In large programs this can involve a number of iterations. In multiproject organizations, where not all projects are using PERT/COST, the steps described in Chapter 3 will have to be carried out.

6. *Cost of Work Report* (Figure 42). The Cost of Work Report is the graphical equivalent of data found on the Financial

	REPORTING ORGN,	CONTRACT NO,	REPORT DATES
ABC — MISSILE AND GHE	XYZ — A&S DIVN	33(600)28369A	TOTAL PROGRAM
LEVEL/SUMMARY ITEM: 37BALLISTIC SHELL 22300		TERM (SPAN):	CUT OFF DATE: 30MAR63
			RELEASE DATE: 10APR63

IDENTIFICATION				MANHOURS				DIRECT COSTS $(000)				TIME	
				WORK TO DATE	TOTALS AT COMPLETION			WORK TO DATE	TOTALS AT COMPLETION				
CHARGE NUMBER	RESP ORGN	PERF ORGN	RES CODE	ACTUAL	PLANNED	LATEST REVISED ESTIMATE	PROJECTED (OVERRUN) UNDERRUN	ACTUAL	PLANNED	LATEST REVISED ESTIMATE	PROJECTED (OVERRUN) UNDERRUN	MOST CRIT SLACK (WKS)	SCHED OR ACT(A) COMPL DATE
ELECTRICAL DESIGN 32164	2217 INSTRUMENTATION	2217	E1	16,900	30,000	31,100	(1,100)	41	90	94	(4)	2.1	25JUL63
			E2	16,800	20,000	20,100	(100)	40	60	60			
		4422	A10	3,500	7,000	7,000		12	25	25			
			M60					5	15	15			
		5514	D1	1,200	5,000	5,000		5	15	15			
			P8	2,800	3,300	3,300		9	10	10			
TOTAL								112	205	209	(.02)(4)		
ELECTRICAL DESIGN, PWR CABLE ASSY 32165		5514	D1	2,200	4,200	4,200		6	12	12		4.2	15JUL63
TOTAL								1,300	2,600	2,500	.04 100		

Fig. 38. PERT/COST Organization Status Report.

ABC – MISSILE AND GHE	REPORTING ORGN.	CONTRACT NO.	REPORT DATES	
LEVEL/SUMMARY ITEM: 4/FIRST STAGE, BALLISTIC SHELL 22300	XYZ – A&S DIVN	33(600)28369A	TERM (SPAN): TOTAL PROGRAM	
			CUT OFF DATE: 30MAR63	
			RELEASE DATE: 10APR63	

MONTH	CHARGE NUMBER	INCREMENTAL COST $(000)				CUMULATIVE COST $(000)				Remarks
		ACTUAL	PLANNED	LATEST REVISED ESTIMATE	(OVER) UNDER PLAN	ACTUAL	PLANNED	LATEST REVISED ESTIMATE	(OVER) UNDER PLAN	
PRIOR	32163					24	24	24	24	Value of Work Performed to date
	32164					92	93	92	92	1) CUM to cut off $6,700,000
	52072					12	12	12	12	2) Latest Month $275,000
	52073					8	8	8		
	78339					2	2	2	2	
	TOTAL					6,150	6,200	6,150	50	
MAR63	32163	1	1	1		25	25	25		(Over) underrun for work performed to June $300,000
	32164	20	19	20	{1}	112	112	112	(1)	
	52072	3	2	3	{1}	115	114	115		
	78339	2	2	2		2	4	2	2	
	TOTAL	250	300	250	50	6,400	6,500	6,400	100	
APR63	32163	1	1	1			26	26		
	32164	6	2	6	(4)		16	21	(5)	
	TOTAL	140	98	140	(42)	6,400	6,598	6,540	58	
TOTAL PERIOD							9,200	9,700	(500)	

Fig. 39. PERT/COST Financial Plan and Status Report.

	REPORTING ORGN.	CONTRACT NO.	REPORT DATES
ABC – MISSILE AND 'GHE	XYZ – A&S DIVN	33(600)28369A	TERM (SPAN): TOTAL PROGRAM
LEVEL/SUMMARY ITEM: 3/BALLISTIC SHELL 22300		CUT OFF DATE: 30MAR63	
			RELEASE DATE: 10APR63

IDENTIFICATION				MANHOURS				TIME
MONTH	RES (SKILL) CODE	PERF ORGN	CHARGE NUMBER	ACTUAL	PLANNED	LATEST REVISED ESTIMATE	(OVER) UNDER PLAN	MOST CRIT SLACK (WKS)
PRIOR	E1	2217	32163	800	2,100	800	1,300	0.0
			32164	13,000	14,000	13,000	1,000	2.1
			32166	2,200	2,200	2,200		16.2
		4422	32163	400	400	400		0.0
			32166	600	600	600		16.2
TOTAL				175,000	179,000	175,000	4,000	0.0
								2.1
MAR63		2217	32163	400	400	400	200	0.0
			32164	3,900	4,100	3,900		2.1
TOTAL								
APR63		2217	32163	95,000	97,000	95,000	2,000	0.0
			32164		4,500	400		2.1
						4,500		
TOTAL					86,000	98,000	(12,000)	
TOTAL				270,000	850,000	856,000	(6,000)	

Fig. 40. PERT/COST Manpower Loading Report.

PROGRAM	CONTRACTOR	CONTRACT NO.	REPORT DATE
MWS	XYZ	ABC-123	10 APR 63

SKILL CODE OR RAINBOW CATEGORY: 72 DESIGNER   SUMMARY ITEM: 22322

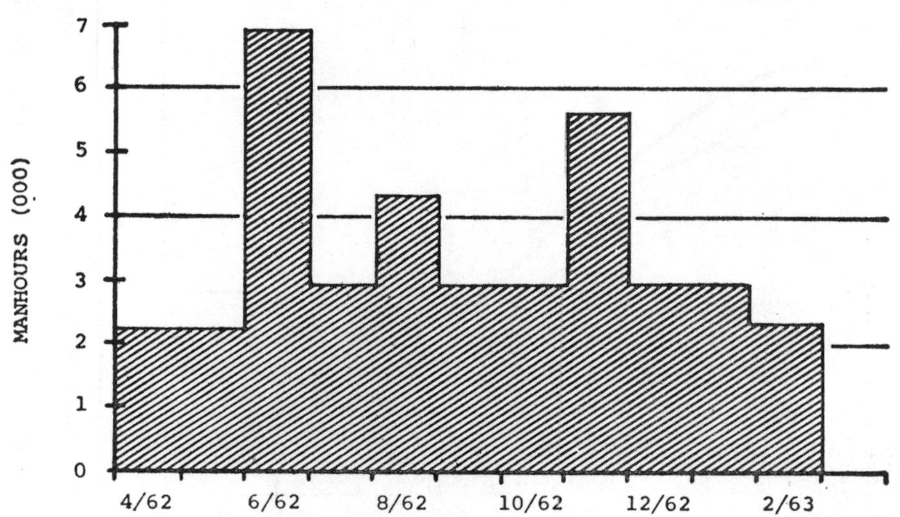

FIG. 41. Manpower loading display.

115

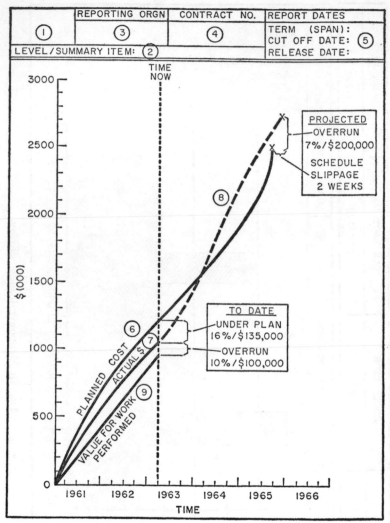

FIG. 42. PERT/COST Cost of Work Report.

Plan and Status Report and Management Summary Report. It emphasizes the "value-of-work-performed" concept and time and cost deviations from plan on both a cumulative-to-date and predicted-at-completion basis. It is intended for higher-level program management in both industry and government.

7. *Cost Outlook and Schedule Outlook Reports* (Figures 43 and 44). These are graphical displays, again generally intended for higher-level program management in both industry and government, showing trend lines, plotted historically, of predicted cost and time deviations from plan. Limit lines or control bands can be introduced at the option of the program manager, which if surpassed will call for higher-management attention, and indicate that cost or time uncertainty should decrease during the life of the program.

Other output reports are available from the basic PERT/ COST system at the option of the user, depending upon the particular computer program being used. These include the Cost Category Report, which represents a synthesis of functional cost elements, such as Engineering, Manufacturing, and Tooling. However, the output reports discussed above generally represent the most significant ones for control purposes. It should be clear that the major emphasis or orientation of these reports is for purposes of program management.

Impact on Organization and Cost

With the inclusion of cost, the introduction of PERT Management Systems has impact outside the program management offices directly concerned with their use. The financial, controller, and auditing organizations will be concerned with the effect of PERT/COST on the company's present accounting system. In this connection there are likely to be changes in such areas as cost account coding structures, methods of handling material costs and commitments, and problems of handling allocation of overhead. It should be emphasized that many of these problems are not uniquely related to PERT/COST. They would arise in the implementation of a detailed cost control system whether it was PERT/COST or not. We shall briefly treat each of the above problem areas in turn.

1. *Cost Account Coding Structure.* In order to get the full benefit out of the management-by-exception principle in

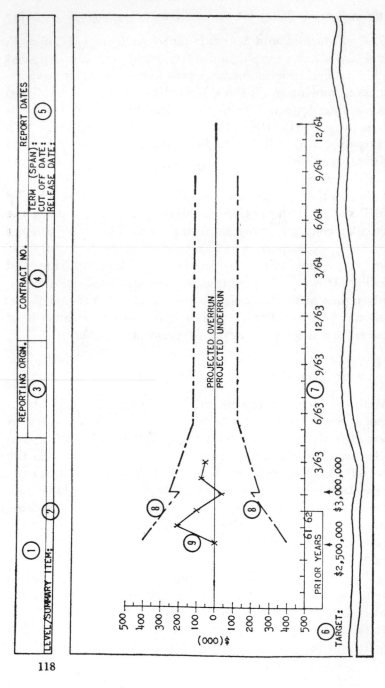

Fig. 43. PERT/COST Cost Outlook Report.

118

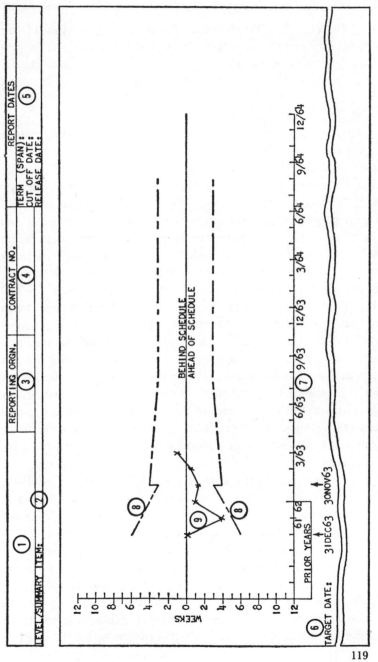

FIG. 44. PERT/COST Schedule Outlook Report.

119

PERT/COST, the Work Breakdown Structure should be coded up in a consistent, hierarchical fashion, as shown in Figure 33. Summary account numbers must be established to the lowest level of the Work Breakdown Structure, i.e., the End Item Subdivision level. It will be recalled that all Work Package charge numbers must be capable of summarization into this end item account number. As long as the accounting system is capable of this, the contractor has a large degree of freedom in establishing Work Package charge numbers which are consistent with his own Work Order or charge numbering system. If the contractor is at a high level of management responsibility in a systems program, however, and many organizations or divisions of the company are involved in the program, he may have to realign internal contract or cost coding structures to meet the overall requirements of the PERT/COST system.

2. *Handling of Material Costs and Commitments.* In the PERT/COST system, "actual costs" include actual expenditures plus "unliquidated commitments." Because of varying procedures in different companies as to what constitutes an unliquidated commitment, and in particular *when* during the process of procuring material it enters this category, the exact definition of an unliquidated commitment is left open to negotiation on each contract. On major systems programs involving many different contractors, however, it is apparent that some uniform practices may have to be developed for consistency in reporting this figure.

Another problem in the area of material costs is the handling of *bulk or common item materials,* which cut across many product-oriented End Item Subdivisions. The possible methods of treatment here are to set up a special high-level End Item Subdivision for such material charges, allocate the charge out to low-level product End Item Subdivisions, or do both, depending upon the requirements of the particular program.

3. *Handling of Overhead.* A problem somewhat similar to the allocation of common material costs exists in connection with the handling of overhead. Should overhead be allocated to

Work Package level or not? Here again we are concerned with policies and procedures which vary among different companies. The policy of some companies is to hold their operating-level personnel responsible for total costs, including applied overhead, but this is not true of all. Clearly, however, total costs including overhead must be reflected in any higher-level PERT/COST report, such as the Management Summary Report. For special categories of overhead, such as corporate general and administration expense, and for fee on the program, special provisions may have to be made in the code numbering within the Work Breakdown Structure.

While the above problems are significant, and decisions are required for the resolution of each one of them, it should be borne in mind that they do not represent the most significant problems connected with successful implementation of PERT/COST. Since these are *program-oriented* management controls, the more important problems are in such areas as the completeness and validity of the Work Breakdown Structure, and the thoroughness and validity with which the PERT/TIME analysis, Work Package cost estimating, and updating are carried out.

A final area of concern to management is the cost of implementing PERT/COST. As in the case of PERT/TIME, more detail is involved than is generally found in most industrial job costing account systems. (It should be emphasized again that this is not always the case.) The cost of implementing PERT/COST is certainly greater than that of implementing PERT/TIME; it is thought to be in the range of 1 to 5 per cent of total project cost, as compared to PERT/TIME alone, which is in the range of 0.5 to 1 per cent. It should be pointed out that these figures may represent learning-curve costs, since extensive experience with PERT/COST has not yet been obtained. In addition, these costs should not be considered as incremental or additive, since clearly a great deal of effort was put into costing systems and estimating methods in prior approaches. The major gains that are being sought from the implementation of basic PERT/COST were stated at the beginning of this chapter, namely, a very significant improvement in both original cost estimating and cost control during the execution phase of the program.

Other PERT/COST Techniques

There are several variations of the PERT/COST technique. One of the more commonly known is termed *time-cost optimization or augmentation,* the model of which was originally developed in connection with CPM.[3] Figure 45 illustrates the principle involved, using a small network for illustrative purposes.

The lower path of the small network in Figure 45 is the critical path, with an initial value of seventeen weeks. For every activity on this network, let us now assume we can obtain a set of "normal" and "crash" time and cost data, as shown in the table of Figure 45. In order to speed up this program for a minimum cost, we will first want to shorten those critical-path activities which give us the *most time acceleration for the least*

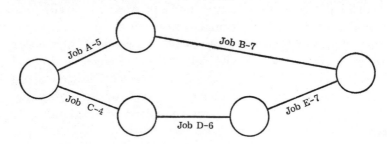

	NORMAL		CRASH		COST SLOPE	1st	2nd	3rd
	Time	Cost	Time	Cost	Dollars/Week	Iteration	Iteration	Iteration
Job A	5	$8K	3	$9.2K	$600			+ $ 600
Job B	7	10K	4	12.1K	700			+ $ 500
Job C	4	6K	3	6.5K	500			−1 + $1100
Job D	6	10K	4	10.8K	400		−2 +$800	
Job E	7	12K	4	12.9K	300	−3 +$900		
	17Wks.	$46K		$51.5K		14 $46.9K	12 $47.7K	11 $ 48.8

FIG. 45. Example of time-cost augmentation.

cost. In other words, we will operate on the critical-path activities which have the smallest cost-time slopes, as shown in Figure
45. After the first operation, or iteration, we will proceed to
the activity with the next smallest cost-time slope.

After two iterations, both paths on the network are of the
same length and are therefore equally critical. We must now
work simultaneously on *both paths* in order to achieve any
further reduction in the schedule. Here again, the principle is
to accelerate activities with the lowest cost-time slopes. The final
result is shown in the table of Figure 45, where after three
iterations, the project can be improved from seventeen to eleven
weeks. It will be noted that cost of the program on a "normal"
basis was $46,000 and that after three iterations an optimized
acceleration cost of $48,800 was achieved. This is in contrast to
the total potential cost of $51,500 shown in Figure 45. With
this model we have achieved maximum program acceleration
for minimum cost. While there is argument about the validity
of such a model, generally in terms of the assumption of linear-
ity between "normal" and "crash" time-cost points, the real
problem of using this time-cost technique is the difficulty of obtaining good data for input to the model.

In addition, we have so far discussed the use of "direct" cost
in this model, i.e., costs which vary directly with time, as shown
in Figure 46. Curve *A* of Figure 46 shows these direct costs and
an "optimum point" which may or may not coincide with the
"normal point." If applied overhead or nondirect costs are now
brought into the picture, as shown in curve *B* of Figure 46, the
optimum time-cost point shifts significantly. This new result is
shown in Figure 46 as the second optimum point, which lies on
a curve representing the addition of both curves *A* and *B*.[4]

If one more cost concept is brought into the model, the
optimum point again shifts. This is the concept of a *penalty
cost,* as shown as curve *C*. This cost might represent the *loss of
profits* resulting from lack of production in a plant which was
not completed at the earliest possible time, or which was down
for maintenance and overhaul. It might also represent the *loss*

in value of a product which did proceed through development,
production, and marketing at the earliest possible time relative
to competing products. If such a penalty-cost curve can actually
be developed, as it sometimes can in the case of "outage" costs

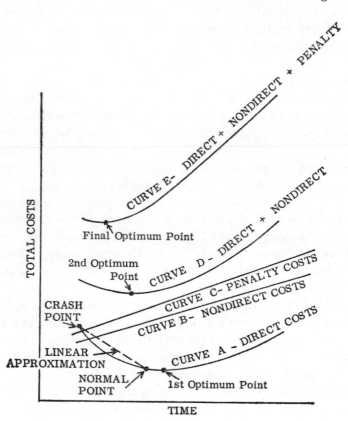

FIG. 46. Assumed time-cost relationships for a job.

during plant overhaul, the results of adding curve *C* to curves
A and *B* will shift the final optimum point, as shown in Figure
46. This concept of penalty cost, or its reverse form, loss in
value, will be discussed again in Chapter 5 in connection with
cost-effectiveness studies, and in Chapter 6 in connection with

multiple-incentive contracting and the principle of value to the government or customer.

REFERENCES

1. *DOD/NASA PERT/COST Guide,* U.S. Government Printing Office, June, 1962.
2. "PERT/COST Output Reports," *DOD/NASA PERT/COST Guide,* Draft Supplement No. 1, 1963.
3. J. E. Kelly and M. R. Walker, "Critical Path Planning and Scheduling," *1959 Proceedings of the Eastern Joint Computer Conference,* pp. 164–167.
4. R. W. Miller, "How to Plan and Control with PERT," *Harvard Business Review,* March–April, 1962, p. 101.

5

The Relationship Between PERT, Project Definition, Systems Engineering, and Configuration Management

Introduction

In Chapters 2 and 4 the basic methodologies of PERT/ TIME and PERT/COST, respectively, were covered. In Chapter 3 implementation problems were discussed. Throughout this material reference has been made to a fundamental assumption underlying the use of PERT techniques. This fundamental assumption—which is often unstated in the literature on the subject—is as follows: Not only the basic objectives of a program but the detailed requirements deriving from them must be clearly specified before PERT Management Systems can be effectively applied. One exception to this principle is the use of PERT/TIME in early planning or conceptual efforts, as described at the end of Chapter 3.

Another way of stating the above assumption is that both program objectives and detailed requirements must be initially well structured, even though there are individual performance, time, and cost uncertainties in achieving these objectives.

127

This latter statement of the principle represents perhaps a subtle but important distinction. It is often overlooked in the controversy that exists covering the validity of objective-oriented planning, particularly for research and development programs. In this connection it should be emphasized that, even though program objectives and detailed requirements must be initially well structured, there is no reason why they cannot be changed during the course of a program if circumstances warrant it. The purpose of this chapter is to discuss the initial structuring of a program where PERT Management Systems are to be applied, and how changes in this initial structuring can be accomplished.

The Argument Against Objective-oriented Planning

Before going into an explanation of how program goals are defined, it is important to discuss the arguments against the objective-oriented assumption underlying the use of PERT Management Systems. These basic arguments can be summarized as follows. Since, in programs of this character (i.e., one-time-through, with associated performance, time, and cost uncertainties), detailed requirements or even basic program objectives are likely to change, why bother with the formal structuring and detailed planning required by techniques such as PERT? Such planning is generally quite difficult to accomplish, and usually more costly (again, depending on the experience and capability of the organization involved). Why not, at the most, do aggregate or "broad-brush" planning and estimating, which is not so difficult, and is less costly and easier to change? Of course, one of the answers to these particular arguments was given in Chapter 1, where we saw historical data on large increases in time and cost of a number of major development programs carried out during the period of the 1950s.

Nevertheless, it is a good idea to take account of these fundamental arguments concerning the use of the objective-oriented approach and detailed planning techniques such as PERT. As we have seen, historical evidence tends to support such a viewpoint; in fact, the arguments given are a clear representation of actual experience on many programs in the past. In addition, these arguments are highly appealing to those who are disposed toward a philosophy in which the world is viewed as a place where goals, and consequently detailed plans, are constantly changing and evolving. Such changes are thought to be the result of circumstances in the external world which cannot be foreseen and controlled, or, more basically, the result of man's inherent inability to establish goals which have any consistency over a period of time. A corollary argument is that the objective-oriented approach may tend to limit the creativity of man, and that he is not necessarily motivated to accomplish preestablished goals.

Flexibility in the Use of PERT

It is the author's view that these arguments must be viewed with a sense of perspective as to when and to what degree they apply, and when they do not. The question often boils down to this: Are the objectives of a given program so important to achieve that it is better to plan, in a meaningful fashion, but subject to change, than not to plan at all? As has been previously stated, PERT Management Systems are not generally applied to programs at the research end of the R & D spectrum. The range of this spectrum includes the areas of pure research, applied research, exploratory development, development and design, and, perhaps, production engineering. In fact, it has been wisely suggested that one way to determine where a project fits into the spectrum is to determine whether it is "PERTable" or not.

It is the author's experience that a large number of programs in the applied research and exploratory development categories have gained significant benefits from the judicious application of PERT techniques. In these applications, however, one must discriminate between those parts of the program which are relatively ill-structured, and not subject to detailed planning, and those which are PERTable in a meaningful fashion. In the development of an entirely new tube or amplifying device, for example, a majority of the activities are usually quite PERTable, while only a minority—though a highly important minority—have to be treated with broader definition, and with more liberal use of time and cost uncertainty estimates. Such an approach becomes quite useful in the case where performance, time, and cost goals are imposed (rightly or wrongly) on programs at this end of the R & D spectrum. Using this approach, it is often quite possible to *replan* the predictable activities in such a manner as to give *more leeway to activities with a high degree of uncertainty,* thus increasing the probability of achieving the overall objectives and requirements.

Furthermore, it is important to note that, even in a program where goals and detailed requirements are clearly established, the experienced PERT analyst will often change his method of approach and amount of detail analyzed during the course of the formal planning exercise. For example, in a hardware development program, there are certain to be many engineering changes after a prototype is tested and drawings are released to production. The number of engineering changes, and the period of time over which they are generated, is largely a function of the tightness of the original program time goal (T_s), the quality and experience of the personnel assigned to the program, and the expected design difficulty of particular units. With these factors in mind, the experienced PERT analyst will not attempt to detail network activities for each individual engineering change, but, rather, he will broadly delineate "redesign" or "continuing engineering" activities after testing and release, and possibly "rework activities" in the initial phase of production, for the particular units involved. The individual time estimates for such overall activities must be based on a knowledge of the factors mentioned previously. Again, later on during the actual execution of the program, if a major change or modification is required, such overall activities may be individually PERTed in more detail. Indeed, it is common practice in programs that undergo a number of *major planned changes* to PERT the effect of each of these modifications by means of a detailed "change model network." The use of PERT is particularly effective here because of the complex relationships involved in the flow of change activity through an organization engaged in both development and production.

The point of this discussion is to show that PERT can be used over a wide variety of situations involving varying levels of detail, when applied with skill and judgment. This judgment includes recognition of the fact that plans can and will change, but the discipline and communication benefits derived from such planning effort are likely to outweigh any arguments for not carrying it out.

For the rigorous application of PERT techniques, however, and particularly PERT/COST in the Work Package form, program objectives and detailed requirements should be clearly established. This initial structuring of a program provides a base line against which changes can be made, but only after the impact against time, cost, and performance factors is evaluated. For large military development programs, the method by which this is done involves the formal processes of Project Definition, systems engineering, and Configuration Management. The principles involved in these disciplines, however, also apply to smaller programs, or any program where the achievement of end goals is of paramount importance to management.

Project Definition

Project Definition involves a formal approach to program planning announced by the Department of Defense in 1962. Program Definition is required by DOD prior to the development and production phase of any major program which falls in the categories of engineering development or operational systems development. These categories in turn fall under the

"RDT & E Program Package" (Research, Development, Test, and Evaluation) of the entire national defense program. It should be emphasized that formal Project Definition is *not* required for the "exploratory"' and "advanced" development categories of the RDT & E budget. It is in these latter categories that new state-of-the-art components may be developed leading to ultimate systems application.

It is not the purpose of this book to describe the details of the "Program Package" system, which is generally associated with the name of Charles J. Hitch, Assistant Secretary of Defense (Comptroller).[1] * It is perhaps sufficient to say that the Program Package system is concerned with the initial top-level planning and budgeting of military programs based upon *missions and end use*, rather than the *functional categories* of military personnel, operation and maintenance, procurement, etc. In this respect, the Program Package system approach is very similar in concept to the product- and task-oriented approach of PERT/COST, although the decision-making area involved is clearly much greater. In a very real sense, the Program Definition and PERT planning and control procedures described in this book represent the follow-up to, or method of executing, those programs which have been approved in the Program Package system.

Despite the fact that Project Definition effort appears to require additional time and money, the viewpoint of the Federal government is that, in the long run, it will produce gains in both these areas. One important point to note is that an exception is made to the requirement for Project Definition in the case of national emergency programs, such as the A-bomb. The following excerpts from a statement of Dr. Harold Brown, Director of Defense Research and Engineering, before the House Committee on Government Operations in May, 1963, give a clear picture of the background and objectives of Project Definition: [2]

---

* Superscript numbers indicate items listed in the References at the end of the chapter.

The research and development program of the Department of Defense has been growing quite rapidly since the Korean War, and rapid growth inevitably produces dislocations and problems. Moreover, there is a limit to the extent of this growth, because there are finite quantities of resources available for research and development. Today, for example, one of our critical shortages is talented manpower. It is, consequently, unwise to try to perform more work than can be adequately staffed and directed. We must be very selective in choosing which work to do, and we must ensure that the efficiency of the work we do is very high. I say this in full awareness of the fact that activities such as basic research are inherently unsuited to being tightly managed, and that there are also inevitable false starts. But well over 50 per cent of our R & D budgets are allocated to Engineering Developments. These two categories can be managed more tightly, because they are really applications engineering jobs, where the technical unknowns are not or should not be the dominating concern. It is, therefore, possible and necessary to make more efficient use of our scientific and engineering resources.... Clearly, if we can inhibit the tendency to huge cost overruns in the Engineering and Operational Systems Development categories, we will have gone a long way towards better planning and better utilization of our scientific and engineering resources....

We have been trying to do something about this cost overrun problem in the past two years. A number of steps: R & D categories, emphasis on providing technological building blocks prior to large systems development, greater use of incentive and fixed price contracting, project definition, better contractor performance evaluation, use of uniform PERT/COST techniques, improved source selection procedures have been taken or are in process. Fundamentally, the only way to avoid such large overruns is to make a careful study before proceeding, allow for the expected "unexpected" problems, and choose a number of developments corresponding to these larger estimates rather than artificially low estimates. The success of any one of these steps is dependent to some extent on the success of the others. They all hang together conceptually and operationally....

Project Definition means paying for detailed engineering and management studies prior to awarding the development contract. Specifications and estimates are refined, familiarity in detail with the problem is gained by the contractor, and major contractor contributions are incorporated into the design. The Project Definition Phase should provide detailed mutual understanding and agreement between the government and the contractor as to what is wanted, how to proceed, and what it will cost in money and time. With this detailed program firmly in hand, the government can then specify which components and subsystems can be obtained by fixed price contracts and which require incentive fee contracts. Not all of the nuts and bolts going into an advanced system require much developing or changing. These components and subsystems can be worked into fairly precise schedules with pre-arranged milestones for monitoring progress.

Of course, such precise performance specifications and milestones are not possible if much technology has to be developed. This is where the "building-block" approach comes into the picture. We believe that all of the basic technology should be on hand prior to systems development. In a rocket system, for example, we should have the materials, technology, and components of the propulsion, airframe and guidance subsystems ready for use. Historically it is evident that many of the subsystems and components that went into our big hardware systems were designed and built prior to and independently of the big systems themselves. The trouble often was that not enough components and subsystems were available, so crash development programs had to be started for the missing items. Because there were substantial technical unknowns involved in this process, specifications changed, time schedules slipped, and other subsystems had to be reconfigured to be compatible with these changes. The effects of this process were in the large cost overruns. Today we are investing substantially in the development of needed technology prior to going all out in hardware development. That is why we must try for greater stability in the research, exploratory and advanced development categories. That is also why the use of the building-block approach is fundamental to project definition. . . .

The application of a Project Definition Phase will help us achieve the following objectives:

1. Define the program.
2. Reduce lead time.
3. Reduce costs.
4. Improve cost and schedule predictions.
5. Improve weapon system effectiveness.
6. Make possible use of fixed price or incentive development contracts.
7. Eliminate "brochuremanship" as a basis for contractor selection.

It will be noted that in discussing the requirements of Project Definition, Dr. Brown places emphasis on the *refinement* of specifications and the *detailing* of time and cost estimates, with the view of reducing to a minimum the remaining uncertainties involved in the program.

This aspect of Project Definition is no more than any prudent business manager should desire—or require—prior to undertaking expenditures on an important new construction program or product development program. In fact, the effort needed to develop such refined specifications and estimates in commercial applications is often represented on a "planning network," as was mentioned at the end of Chapter 3. There it was pointed out that many large companies plan all marketing, engineering, and manufacturing actions prior to making a Go-No-Go decision on a new-product program. The major difference between the majority of these applications and the DOD situation is the *complexity* of the technical interrelationships between the various end items of a military or space program. Thus, one important part of Project Definition concerns itself with the problems of *technical systems analysis,* and this aspect of Project Definition has a major impact on the kind of engineering known as "systems engineering."

Systems Engineering

Systems engineering emerged as a distinct area of specialization with the onset of large and complex new weapon or weapon system developments of the 1950s. As with any other new field of specialization, it is possible to trace its origins to an earlier date. It can be noted, however, that the first book devoted entirely to the subject was published in 1957.[3]

In a certain sense, the systems engineer bears the same relationship to the development and design engineer as does the research scientist. The systems engineer is not directly concerned with the detailed problems of development and design. In addition, the bulk of his work must precede that of development and design engineering. However, the systems engineer is concerned with a very different set of problems than the research scientist. Rather than seeking new concepts, or an understanding of the processes of nature, he is concerned with examining the *best possible ways* of achieving the primary goals of a program, or the "mission effectiveness" of a weapon system, by utilizing existing or "within-the-state-of-the-art" technology. Then he is concerned with "optimizing" or making the best possible trade-offs between performance factors such as range, payload, and reliability, and in turn making trade-offs of these against time and cost factors. When all this has been done, he must make explicit recommendations for a system which will have an acceptable "cost-effectiveness" ratio.

If these requirements of systems analysis are difficult enough in themselves, the job of the systems engineer is made even more complex by the difficulty of defining the "effectiveness" or "value" of the system with which he is concerned. In the weapons system case, this effectiveness may depend on future enemy developments about which he may have little or no information. This concept of effectiveness or value for military development programs is analogous to the problem of the businessman who is launching a new product and who is concerned about how the product will fare in the marketplace, and in particular, how it will stand up against competitive new-product developments. Figure 47 is a graphical portrayal of this concept of value, adapted from Forrester.[4] It will be noted from Figure 47 that, conceptually, value is at a low or even negative figure during an early period of time when the product, if it were introduced, would be too advanced in character to be marketable. The reason for the negative figure is the invest-ment in development costs with no recovery from sales. Figure

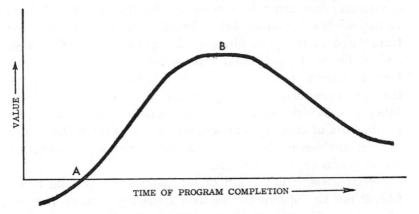

FIG. 47. Value of development program results.

47 shows a peaking of the value or acceptability of the product, after which value declines with the passage of time. It is this declining part of the value curve which we were concerned with (in its reciprocal form) in Figure 46 in Chapter 4. It will be recalled that there we discussed the concept of a penalty cost (curve *C* of Figure 46), i.e., the cost of not bringing a product onto the market at the earliest possible time.

In the military domain, the systems engineer is also con-cerned with the peak and declining portions of the value or effectiveness curve. Another way of saying this is that he is concerned with the increasing penalty cost to the national de-fense for not having an important new weapon system developed in time to meet an enemy threat. It is for these basic reasons that time goals are often as important as performance goals in military development programs. As we have seen in recent years, because of the resource-limitation problem, cost has been added as an equally important goal in the establishment of military development programs. It should be clear that the difficulties of quantifying such a value or effectiveness curve for either military or commercial development programs are very great.

With such difficulties involved in the conceptual framework of systems engineering, it is small wonder that its methodology, or approaches to system definition, have not been very well formulated in the past. Since its inception, the methodology and results of any particular systems analysis effort have often been dependent more on the approach of the individual systems engineer than anything else. In addition, because of the inherent difficulties of the subject, there has been a tendency on the part of many systems engineers not to carry the results of their analyses to the point of a concrete set of performance specifications or requirements.

Nevertheless, it is the job of the systems engineering to define, if not an "optimum," at least a sharply reduced number of "satisficing" system configurations out of all the possibilities that exist. Until this is done, it is impossible to establish a meaningful system hardware or product breakdown with an associated set of end item performance requirements. These results of systems engineering are necessary to establish the product-oriented End Item Subdivisions of the PERT/COST Work Breakdown Structure. As has been pointed out in both Chapters 2 and 4, it is not possible to carry out meaningful PERT/TIME analysis (with emphasis on validity of critical-path analysis) or PERT/COST estimating (with emphasis on costing at the Work Package level) until the Work Breakdown Structure has been defined in this manner and the substance of the work for each product-oriented End Item Subdivision within it understood.

Thus, systems engineering occupies a most significant role in the Program Definition process and in the establishment of meaningful PERT/TIME and PERT/COST analysis. A brief treatment will be given of the methodology of systems engineering as it has developed in recent times in connection with major military and space programs.

Systems Engineering Methodology

After conceptual efforts, Program Definition and the start of the systems engineering process begin with a statement of the broad goals of the program as established by the government. These generally include the *primary mission goals,* along with the *major performance goals,* such as payload range and reliability for a new weapon or space program. In addition, data on the environment in which the system must operate are generally given. For the reasons pointed out in the previous section, cost and time goals might be given as an overall constraint on the final configuration, along with technical performance goals and environmental constraints. It should be emphasized that the concept of cost involved here is a *total one;* that is, it includes not only development and testing costs but production costs (including possibly unit product cost objectives) along with logistical costs, i.e., operating and maintenance. In the Program Package system of the Federal government, these three elements of total cost are referred to as "research and development," "investment," and "operating" costs.

Although these initial program goals, particularly in the area of costs, may be established on an extremely gross basis and possess considerable uncertainty, they will be examined in greater detail as systems analysis proceeds. This is because one of the important outputs of the process is a cost-effectiveness study, of the type mentioned previously, for the proposed new system. It should be emphasized that during the systems analysis process, we are not dealing with PERT/COST Work Package detail in connection with the costs of the development program. Rather, we are involved with *aggregate estimates* of all three elements of total cost, made from costing models or other cost "guesstimating" techniques, generally based on extrapolation and use of *cost estimating relationships* obtained from prior programs. It may be mentioned, parenthetically, that such data are generally inadequate, and a good deal of effort is being expended at the present time to improve it. One approach is to establish much improved "cost data banks" which will be based upon a large amount of historical data. In the development area, it is believed that such data will be improved by addition of PERT/COST inputs, which specifically relate development tasks to costs and provide a better basis for cost extrapolation.

After the overall mission and performance goals have been refined, or understood, to the satisfaction of the systems engineer, the next step is to establish explicit *measures of effectiveness* for the system. These measures will be used later to test whether or not, or to what degree, the overall technical effectiveness of the system is being achieved. After these measures of effectiveness have been established, a *mathematical model* or *effectiveness model* of the system may be developed. In large systems programs, additional mathematical models, such as *reliability, maintainability, and availability models,* are developed. When more exact figures for various technical parameters are developed and exercised through these models, the choice of the ones providing the best overall system effectiveness will be possible, and will thus help establish the "cost-effectiveness ratio" of the system.

Meanwhile, *functional analysis* of the system can begin. This phase of systems engineering is concerned with the basic functions which must be performed during the actual operation of the system when it is finally put into use, and therefore will be realized in hardware. For example, the typical "top-level" functions which must be performed in a missile firing are countdown, ignition, propulsion, staging, guidance, separation, and reentry. After these top-level functions have been identified, *lower-level functional flow diagrams* are developed.

Concerning this important stage of the systems engineering process, a quotation from an Air Force manual on the relationship of functional analysis to equipment design is appropriate: [5]

> As additional detailed flow diagrams are prepared for the operational system, the contractor should carefully examine the possibilities of trade-offs between functions, e.g., it is possible that a computing function that is required for status monitoring can be adequately combined with a computing function required for missile guidance. One primary reason for employing the functional flow methodology is to provide a technique for systematically considering a number of possible alternate functions and flows which will meet system requirements. A maximum effort should therefore be conducted during this early phase of program definition to select from the possible alternatives the set of flow diagrams which best meets system requirements in terms of cost, time and performance. The trade-offs made at this time shall be carefully weighed in making decisions concerning predicted automation, mechanization and man-equipment interface requirements of alternate functions. Caution should be exercised to avoid using preconceived equipment configurations as the basis for portraying systems functions. Except where system requirements specify automation, mechanization and man-equipment interface, or alternate functions arise for selection, the functions shall not state automation, mechanization or man-equipment interface requirements. The requirement for limiting functional flow block diagrams to pure functions is specifically designed to permit maximum latitude for accomplishing equipment trade-offs later in the system analysis program, thereby providing the opportunity for a wide selection of possible design solutions. Such a technique will increase the probability of best solution choice. On the other hand, preconceived equipment configurations will only serve to limit possible alternatives and restrict solution choice.

The next step in the process is to translate these low-level functional diagrams into *design requirements,* keeping in mind the constraints imposed by current design technology and what can be developed within the state of the art. This generally involves liaison with personnel skilled in specialized areas of design. The establishment of design requirements on the basis of functional analysis provides the means for grouping or identifying the *subsystem breakdown* of the system. (This subsystem breakdown becomes, in practice, the basis of the Work Breakdown Structure in PERT/COST.) The same approach is used in establishing the design requirements for special ancillary equipment and facilities, such as ground support equipment and facilities, or even the requirements of the *personnel subsystem*. In establishing these design requirements, consideration is given to such constraints as weight, power, volume, environmental factors, reliability, operability, safety, and human performance factors.

It is important to emphasize the magnitude of the problem in the systems engineering process at this point. Suppose, after functional analysis, the total system is determined to have six basic subsystems. Let us also suppose, for the sake of simplicity, that two alternative design approaches are proposed for each of these six subsystems. This results theoretically in 2^6, or 64 initial possible system configurations. Of course, many of these possible configurations can be discarded as being outside the overall performance goals (and possibly time and cost goals) for the total system. To narrow the selection down further, *parametric studies* to determine the most "sensitive" or important technical parameters affecting system effectiveness are next made. When the choice is narrowed down to a few, performance requirements figures for such factors as reliability, weight, and power must be established not only for the system but for the lower-level subsystems, and alternative design approaches must be defined, if there is more than one. If cost and time are real restraints (as they usually are), estimates for these must be developed for each design alternative, even though this is done on an aggregate or cost modeling basis, as mentioned previously. If the program involves potentially high production volume, unit production costs may be a real restraint and have to be estimated and factored into the analysis at this point. In order to establish logistical or operating costs, various personnel requirements studies will also have to be factored into the analysis. The introduction of logistical or operating considerations poses very difficult problems, but they must be considered in any complete systems analysis effort.

When the process of systems analysis has reached this stage, it is possible to choose a *preliminary or base-line system configuration*. This may be done basically by inspecting the final data, arranged in matrix form, and choosing the system which comes closest to meeting the overall system goals, including time and cost goals. It may also be done by establishing an explicit *figure of merit* for each element of the proposed system, and picking the one with the highest figure. J. A. Boose of IBM has described a numerical approach whereby such factors as reliability, weight, cost, and time to develop can all be placed on a common frame of reference to produce such an overall figure of merit.[6] The process involves assigning dimensionless numbers representing plus or minus deviations from individual system goals and adding these dimensionless figures to a final algebraic total.

Whichever approach is used, there will usually be a number of iterations before the choice of final system configuration is made. It should be remembered that this final system configuration is really the initial or base-line system configuration, since some elements of the system will undoubtedly change as difficulties are experienced during the course of development or if overall program requirements change for any external reason. Nevertheless, the process of systems engineering to this point has resulted in an integrated analysis of the constitutent elements of the system. These elements represent hardware end item design requirements or end item performance specifications. It should be emphasized that this is an *integrated* set of performance requirements—i.e., these specifications represent "design-to" requirements for individual hardware items based upon a complete analysis of total system requirements, including important interfaces. They do not establish the actual designs; this will be done during the course of the development program.

The establishment of the base-line system configuration— sometimes referred to as the *base-line design requirement* [7]— is a major milestone in the systems engineering process under Project Definition. From this base line, the Work Breakdown Structure can be established down to the end item level on a meaningful basis, and detailed PERT/TIME and PERT/COST analyses can be effectively carried out. One approach by which the definition of End Item technical parameters is specifically related to the Work Breakdown Structure is called the *Specification Tree*. Another, called the *Work Breakdown Structure Requirements Plan*—is described in Army Materiel Command Regulation 11–16 on Planning and Control Techniques for Project Management.[8] If, at the end of this total process, the overall cost effectiveness of the system is judged to be satisfactory in terms of comparison with both other "friendly" systems and possible enemy systems, the program is ready to go into the development phase, and the Project Definition phase is ended. It is also ready for the beginning of a control approach known as Configuration Management. It should be clear to the reader that the complex process of Systems Definition is susceptible to a PERT/TIME analysis. Indeed, this is commonly done, but use of PERT/COST is not generally required for this stage of a program.

Configuration Management

Before discussing the subject of Configuration Management, we shall turn first to the subject of its predecessor, *configuration control*. Configuration control is an established practice in industry, and, in fact, has long been carried out under the name of engineering change control. The term *configuration* in this context refers to identification of the product through formally prepared drawings. The term *configuration control* refers to the specific procedures by which any changes to these drawings are proposed, approved, recorded, and distributed. Because configuration control, in the classical sense, begins at a point where drawings have been *released to production,* these procedures are usually highly formalized and comprehensive. The point at which approved drawings are available for release to production is sometimes called the *base-line configuration point,* in contrast to the *base-line design requirement point* discussed previously. In an ideally executed program, the establishment of the base-line design configuration occurs *after* prototypes of the product have been fabricated, assembled, and tested. In a crash program, or programs with a high degree of concurrency, i.e., development and production are overlapped, the base-line design configuration and the release of drawings to production may occur *prior to* prototype testing.

After the base-line design configuration point has been reached and drawings have been released to production, expenditures for the procurement of production materials, tooling, and the establishment of special production and testing facilities go up very rapidly. In addition, based upon these same drawings, expenditures are being incurred on spare-parts provisioning lists, maintenance handbooks, and similar documentation requirements. In a commercially oriented program, expenditures are also being incurred on the preparation of sales and advertising material, such as data sheets and product brochures. Hence the necessity for a highly procedurized approach in any established configuration or change control system, including a specialized drawing and change document numbering system and the review and approval of many individuals throughout the organization.

The relationship of PERT to the engineering change phase of a program was mentioned early in this chapter. After initial drawing release, a flow of changes is to be expected in most programs. The PERT analyst will seek to establish an "overall continuing engineering" activity representing this effort, and possibly "rework activities" for particular units in the initial phase of production. However, when a *major change or modification* to the product is proposed, or found to be necessary, the PERT analyst may develop a detailed subnetwork for the individual change. This subnetwork will be inserted in the overall program network, showing the all required change activities, including procedural activities. As was mentioned previously, a model change network is often useful at this point, but individual time estimates should be made for each activity on a major change or "modification" package. The process of configuration control continues until the last engineering change in the program has been approved, recorded, and made effective on all production units, as specified by the change document. Thus the process of configuration control continues throughout the life of the program, but at a decreasing rate of engineering change proposals or change orders.

The concept of Configuration Management as developed by the Air Force, is considerably broader than the process of configuration control as it has just been described. It goes back, in fact, to the end of the systems analysis and definition phase, where the *base-line design requirement* was established.

The realization that some earlier form of control was required on system *end item or product identification* came about on the ICBM programs of the late 1950s. These crash programs—such as Atlas, Titan, and Minuteman—were handled on a *concurrent basis;* i.e., development, production, and site deployment were all overlapped in order to meet a critical operational readiness date. Figure 48 shows this concurrency principle in graphical form and illustrates the concept of Configuration Management as an increasing slope of product definition from the earliest phases of the program.[9] Because of the many important interfaces between the various subsystems of a total ICBM system and the necessity of keeping track of changes to these interfaces during development, while at the same time spending millions of dollars on concurrent production buildup and site activation, something more than change control on production release drawings was obviously required. Thus Configuration Management emerged as a complete approach to product identification, control, and status accounting on a large systems acquisition program.

The difference between product definition and project definition is worth emphasizing at this point. It will be recalled that a major output of systems engineering during the

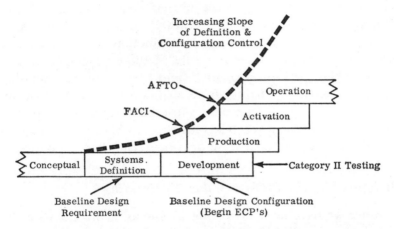

FIG. 48. Systems Definition and Configuration Management.

Project Definition phase was the base-line design requirement, including end item performance requirements or specifications. This established the first *product definition* of the program. The *specific resources and time* required to develop this product were established by PERT/TIME and PERT/COST analysis in the final phase of the process of *Project Definition*.

During the course of development, the initial product definition or base line undergoes change and refinement, and is ultimately reflected in a set of detailed assembly and component or part drawings, along with bill-of-material lists. Correspondingly, if it becomes necessary for any reason to change the baseline design requirement established during Project Definition in any significant way, some portions of the PERT /TIME schedule and PERT/COST Work Package plan are certain to be affected, and require changes.

Thus the first phase of Configuration Management involves a formal control procedure over changes to the base-line design requirement, with emphasis on revision to individual lower-level performance requirements. These can only be changed after the appropriate review with systems engineering, development and design engineering, and management and customer if there is a significant impact on performance, time, and cost factors for the overall system. Clearly, then, the function of Configuration Management, in conjunction with systems engineering, plays an important role in those development programs where performance, time, and cost goals are operating simultaneously. In Chapter 6 we shall see that the mechanism of Configuration Management must be preserved in connection with multiple-incentive contracting, whether the program is being carried out on a crash or concurrency basis or not.

Relationship of PERT to Value Engineering

Since we have been discussing problems connected with the development and design phase of the program, we shall pause briefly to consider the relationship of PERT Management Systems to *value engineering* at this stage.

Value engineering, as the term is generally understood, is concerned with reducing the cost of units or equipments which go into production. While value engineering analysis of product designs may take place *after* drawings have been released to production, this is not as effective an approach as when it is carried out on a concurrent basis with development and design. This is because there is always some penalty cost associated with introducing a design change after drawings have been released to production, which offset basic savings.

It will be recalled that one of the constraints which can be placed upon initial systems design for programs with a high-volume production potential is the achievement of a *unit product cost objective.* If, during the course of development and design, it appears that this figure will be exceeded, value engineering makes specific recommendations to bring it back within target. In addition, value engineering participates in design reviews of all elements of the system, and makes recommendations concerning alternate, lower-cost designs.

Thus, the role of value engineering during the development and design program is a significant one, and its efforts should be included in the PERT network for this phase of the program. In addition, there is one aspect of PERT analysis which is of special interest to the value engineer. When a program is conducted under tight schedule conditions, the value engineer often has difficulty getting his recommendations implemented owing to scarcity of time. In this situation, an analysis of PERT data will reveal opportunities for carrying out value engineering on those portions of the design program where positive slack conditions exist.

Finally, the value engineer may be able to contribute to the reduction of development costs as well as production costs. After reviewing the development and design program, he may be able to recommend existing designs which are acceptable, rather than undertaking a new development. If this recommendation is accepted, the appropriate activities on the network, and associated costs, may be deleted from the development phase of the program.

Integration of Performance, Time, and Cost

Figure 49 gives a graphical view of the overall relationships between PERT Management Systems and the major areas discussed in this chapter, namely, Project Definition, systems engineering, and Configuration Management. It is adapted from an Air Force publication on the subject of Program Definition.[10] It will be noted in Figure 49 that formal Project Definition does not begin until after the early conceptual and feasibility phase has been completed. Another way of saying this is

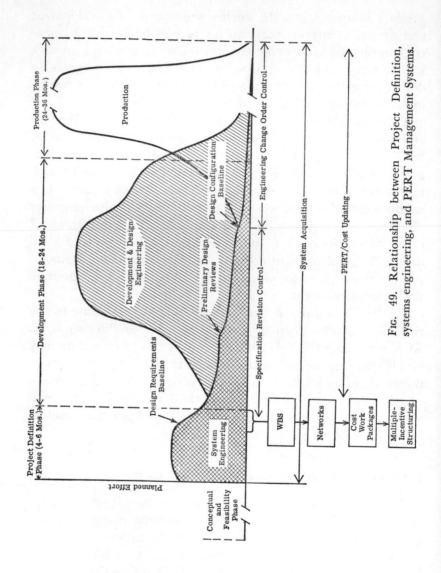

Fig. 49. Relationship between Project Definition, systems engineering, and PERT Management Systems.

that Project Definition does not begin until the program is thought to be technologically feasible, as was emphasized in the quotation previously given from testimony of Dr. Harold Brown, Director of Defense Research and Engineering. It will also be noted in Figure 49 that PERT Management Systems are not indicated as applying to this early phase, although in Chapter 3 we discussed how PERT/TIME can be usefully applied to exploratory development programs when used with skill and judgment. However, the use of well-defined goals and tight management controls is not generally advisable at this stage of program evolution.

Project Definition is usually carried out in the Department of Defense by placing two equally funded contracts with competing contractors. We have mentioned that typical inputs to the start of the Project Definition process are the results of prior feasibility studies, along with mission goals and basic performance, time, and cost objectives. It will be noted in Figure 49 that systems engineering effort is at its highest level during the early portion of the Project Definition phase. After the base-line design requirement has been established, systems engineering effort goes down rapidly, but continues on into the development program at a lower level. PERT/TIME and PERT/COST analyses based upon the base-line design requirement, plus contract negotiations for the follow-up development phase, complete the process of Project Definition. There are three possible results at the end of such a Program Definition effort:

1. The program may be terminated at this point because of an unsatisfactory cost-effectiveness ratio.
2. The Project Definition effort may be continued further in order to change or refine the base-line system or cost and schedule projections.
3. The program may be authorized to proceed into development, although approval for production may not be given at this time.

Figure 49 indicates other important features of the acquisition process discussed in prior sections, such as the period of specification revision, base-line design configuration, and the period of change control. It also indicates important joint customer-industry *design reviews,* such as the preliminary design review and configuration design review. It should be emphasized that these design reviews, along with similar ones carried out internally by industry, are one of the single most important vehicles for obtaining a true measure of technical progress. It will be recalled in Chapter 3, in connection with updating, that the PERT analyst was encouraged to attend all such design reviews in order to obtain insight into the actual design progress of the program. Thus, measurement against the detailed performance-time-cost plan set up during the Project Definition phase, plus any changes to it made through Configuration Management, is possible through the mechanism of design reviews, PERT/TIME updating, and PERT/COST reporting.

The reader should note that, as a result of the entire process depicted in Figure 49, the factors of performance, time, and cost have been brought together in such a way as to provide the basis for an integrated management system for development programs. The achievement of this important goal—mentioned in Chapter 1 as one of the major objectives for improved management of such programs—has not often been fully understood or recognized.

The integration of the performance, time, and cost variables is perhaps best illustrated by reference to Figure 50, which is an adaptation of a figure in the *NASA PERT and Companion Cost System Handbook.*[11]

Here we see the program broken down in to a three-dimensional view. The Work Breakdown Structure provides the basic framework for defining all the product-oriented and non-product-oriented tasks required to achieve the goals of the program. As we have seen, a comprehensive process of systems engineering has produced a base-line set of performance specifications, which are associated with the End Item Subdivisions of the Work Breakdown Structure. The complete process of PERT/TIME network planning and replanning has been carried out for each of these End Item Subdivisions, and PERT/COST Work Package estimates have been established which are explicitly tied to the networks. If, during the execution of the development program, there are any significant changes to the base-line system, these will be controlled through *Configu-*

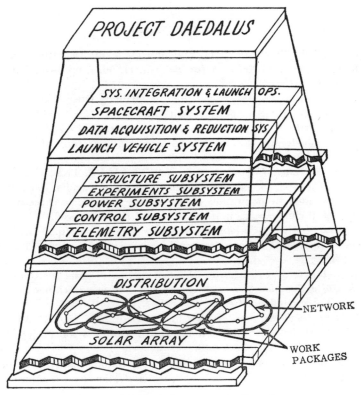

Fig 50. Integration of time, cost, and performance.

ration Management. No matter at what level these changes occur, they can be reflected down through the appropriate hierarchy of the Work Breakdown Structure, and the impact on affected time networks and Cost Work Packages can be assessed. Thus performance, time, and cost parameters for the development program have been related in one integrated program management system. This integration can, in principle, be achieved on any program where PERT Management Systems are used. Only the degree of implementation will vary, depending on the size, complexity, and importance of the program.

REFERENCES

1. C. J. Hitch, "Plans, Programs and Budgets in the Department of Defense," *Operations Research Journal*, vol. 11, no. 1, pp. 1–18, January–February, 1963.
2. Dr. Harold Brown, statement before the Military Operations Sub-Committee, Committee on Government Operations, May 21, 1963. (Statement actually read by the Deputy Director, Dr. Fubini.)
3. H. H. Goode and R. E. Machol, *Systems Engineering*, McGraw-Hill Book Company, Inc., New York, 1957.
4. J. W. Forrester, *Industrial Dynamics*, The M.I.T. Press, Cambridge, Mass., 1961, p. 326. Reprinted from Industrial Dynamics, 1961, by Jay W. Forrester, by permission of the M.I.T. Press, Massachusetts Institute of Technology, Cambridge, Mass. All rights reserved.
5. *Systems Analysis: Procedures for System Definition*, Hq. Ballistic Systems Division, Air Force Systems Command, USAF, June, 1962, Par. 3.2.3.2.
6. J. A. Boose, *A Non-intuitive Decision-making Method for Configuration of a Complex System*, International Business Machines Corporation, Space Guidance Center, Oswego, N.Y., April, 1963.
7. *Systems Analysis: Procedures for System Definition*, pp. 3-12–3-13.
8. AMCR 11–16, "Planning and Control Techniques for Project Management," vol. II, pp. 5.8–5.10.
9. B. N. Bellis, "The Requirements for Configuration Management during Concurrency," Air Force Systems Command Management Conference, Monterey, Calif., May, 1962.
10. *Program Definition Phase*, Hq. Air Force Systems Command, USAF, February, 1963, pp. 38–43.
11. *NASA PERT and Companion Cost System Handbook*, Oct. 30, 1962, p. 11-2.

6

The Relationship Between PERT Management Systems, Organization, and Profits

Introduction

The reader will recognize that PERT Management Systems, in association with systems engineering and Configuration Management, are certain to have significant impact on organization structure and profits. In this chapter we shall first discuss the various methods of organizing to implement these techniques. Throughout it has been emphasized that the frame of reference for the application of these systems is in the area of *program management*. As we have seen, in the case of large-scale development undertakings, the responsibilities of program management require an integrated approach to the planning and control of the factors of performance, time, and cost. This same principle applies to other one-time-through programs, such as installation of a new data-processing system or construction of a new pilot plant, although the methodology for establishing initial performance specifications and for keeping track of changes to them may not be so complex, nor the uncertainty factor as significant.

155

One test of whether or not a given organization is ready for the use of PERT Management Systems is the degree to which its present organization is already project-oriented. If, in order to carry out the work of the organization, it has been found necessary to establish such titles as "project engineer" or "program manager," which have responsibilities that cut across established functional or departmental lines, then the organization is likely to benefit from the proper application of PERT Management Systems. No matter how vaguely such a position is defined, the fact is that the *general management* has found it necessary to establish a new position, presumably representing an extension of its own responsibility and authority, which is specifically concerned with the management of a given program throughout the organization.

Matrix Organization

Figure 51 illustrates such a program management approach in a conventional or functionally structured organization. The approach is sometimes called a *matrix organization,* since functional or straight-line responsibility extends vertically downward from each major functional department head, and program responsibility extends horizontally across the organization from each of the various program managers. Though the matrix structure appears to violate classic management principles for delegation of authority and responsibility, it has become a way of life for those organizations engaged in carrying out complex, one-time-through programs. This is not to say that there are not many difficulties involved in such a structure, as every experienced government and industry program manager knows. For example, the attempt to solve the problem of command by making "project assignments," while not changing reporting responsibility, is one of these.

Another approach is to place the functional organizations in a "service" role to the program management offices.[1] * In ex-

---

* Superscript numbers indicate items listed in the References at the end of the chapter.

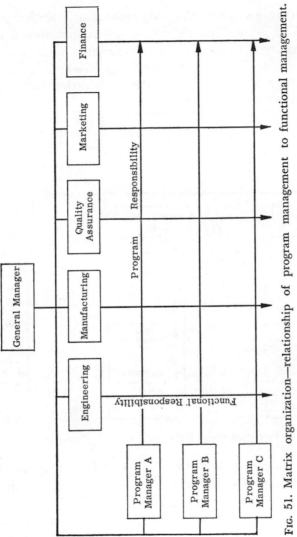

FIG. 51. Matrix organization—relationship of program management to functional management.

treme situations, where the requirements of meeting particular program objectives override those of maintaining a balanced functional organization, it has sometimes been necessary to revert to a complete "projectized" approach, as shown in Figure 52. This approach also has its difficulties, including addi-

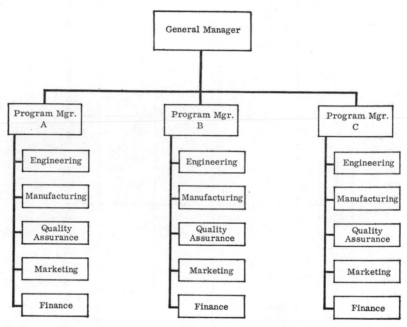

FIG. 52. Completely "projectized" organization.

tional costs, although in the short run it may appear to solve some serious problems. Over the long run, however, in a multi-project organization the problems of a highly projectized approach become apparent. As programs phase in and out, there is difficulty in balancing work loads, and personnel become greatly concerned with their future, particularly where there is no apparent steady line of progression. The use of various administrative devices, such as the establishment of overhead activities for personnel "between projects," rarely alleviates, and often aggravates, these problems. Thus, in order to maintain a viable organization for the long run, it is common for organizations engaged in multiproject work to adopt the matrix organization structure, or some version of it.

Program Management Structure

The problem then becomes one of determining to what size and depth the program management group, within the framework of the matrix structure, should be organized. In many industries, where the complexity or innovative features of the product are relatively low, and the procedures and standards by which products or programs pass between functional areas are well established, it may not be necessary to have anything more than a single project engineer located within the engineering function. If, however, the program is a large one involving a complex new product, and the interactions between functional areas of the organization for handling such products are not well established, the program management office will have to be staffed in considerable size and depth. Figure 53 shows the structure of a program management office for a large, complex program involving both development and production. It will be noted that the program manager has a functional counterpart reporting to him for many of the major functions in the organization. In addition, because of the particular requirements of his program, he may have specialized "line functions" reporting to him which are not found elsewhere in the organization. An overseas installation and check-out group might be an example of such a specialized function.

Most important, however, in order for him to exercise his program management and decision-making authority in the areas of performance, time, and cost, are the three organizational elements shown directly underneath the Program Manager in Figure 53. These three elements are Systems Engineering, Program Planning and Control, and Configuration Management. They represent the organizational structure by which

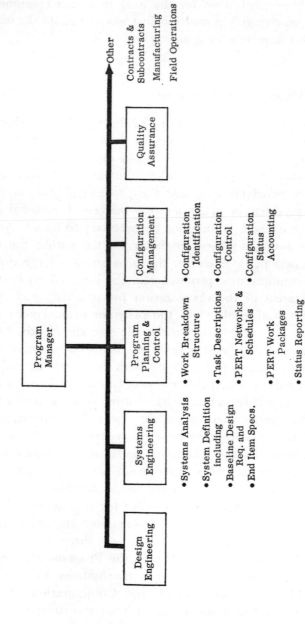

Fig. 53. Organization of a program management office.

Program Manager

Design Engineering

Systems Engineering
- Systems Analysis
- System Definition including
- Baseline Design Req. and
- End Item Specs.

Program Planning & Control
- Work Breakdown Structure
- Task Descriptions
- PERT Networks & Schedules
- PERT Work Packages
- Status Reporting

Configuration Management
- Configuration Identification
- Configuration Control
- Configuration Status Accounting

Quality Assurance

Other
Contracts & Subcontracts
Manufacturing
Field Operations

160

the Program Manager implements the management systems which have been described in this book.

It will be noted under Systems Engineering that the basic responsibilities described in Chapter 5 are shown. The last items indicated are the establishment of the base-line design requirement along with end item performance specifications. These outputs of Systems Engineering provide the basis for the Work Breakdown Structure maintained by Program Planning and Control and the initial Configuration Identification data maintained by the Configuration Management group. Changes to these base-line data involve the same three groups, with Configuration Management responsible for implementing the basic control procedures, as described in Chapter 5.

With this organization approach, the function of Program Planning and Control becomes a vital element of the program manager's office. The vehicle of the Work Breakdown Structure, and PERT/TIME and PERT/COST predictions and analysis of any basic changes, allows the program manager to *interrelate* the key variables of performance, time, and cost as he goes through the program execution phase. In addition, if reporting or updating information is prompt and accurate and related to detailed time networks and Cost Work Packages, the program manager has an excellent view of the status of work being carried out on his program in each functional organization, even though this work is not under his direct control. In fact, the proper implementation of PERT Management Systems will actually give the program manager the opportunity to exercise the responsibility for which he is charged. It is perhaps obvious to say that these systems will not replace the ability and judgment of an individual program manager. Nevertheless, properly implemented, they provide powerful tools for one of the most difficult areas of modern industry management practice, namely, program management within the framework of the matrix organization.

Thus far in this discussion it has been emphasized that the actual implementation of PERT systems on a particular program is the responsibility of the program management office, particularly through the function of Program Planning and Control. This is a natural consequence of the fact that these systems were specifically developed for program-oriented effort. It should be pointed out, however, that the day-to-day management of a particular Cost Work Package, or a group of activities on a time network, is properly the responsibility of operating-level supervision in the functional area involved. It will also be be recalled that the manager of each functional department receives a report on the time and cost status of all Work Package effort within his area of responsibility. This is the Organization Status Report of the PERT/COST system, shown in Figure 38 in Chapter 4.

The program manager is concerned with the *net impact* on his program of cost performance on many Work Packages, or of the activities on the time network which have critical-path significance. Therefore, when a large amount of negative slack or cost overrun is indicated in either the Management Summary or the Program/Project Status Report, the program manager will certainly wish to be apprised of the detailed problems involved. Thus, the astute program manager will abstain from the day-to-day problems in the functional management area, and only involve himself where he needs to on a true management-by-exception basis.

Central PERT Staff

Thus far we have discussed the implementation of PERT Management Systems in terms of a Program Planning and Control function under a well-organized program management office. What about the application of PERT to small projects, which do not justify such a program management structure?

In most organizations there is need for a central staff group with a high capability in PERT Management Systems. This staff can be kept fairly small, if implementation on larger programs is carried out by the individual program management offices. The responsibilities of such a central PERT staff may include the following:

1. Keeping abreast of new developments in the field of PERT Management Systems; advising general management of new requirements and need for changes in the organization's policy with respect to these systems.

2. Exercising leadership in establishing internal PERT procedures, if the organization has not yet developed them. This usually involves heading up a task force effort, since almost every functional area of the organization is involved.

3. Carrying out or supervising the conduct of training programs for all personnel who need to work with these systems.

4. Assisting the implementation of PERT on small programs or proposal efforts, where a program management organization has not yet been established.

5. Recruiting and providing PERT specialists for assignment to the program management groups.

6. Providing a service function, in the area of data processing, to the various program management offices. It is not likely, or indeed particularly desirable, that the data-processing equipment and facility be under the cognizance of the central PERT staff. However, it is very likely that personnel who have specialized in both PERT and data-processing techniques will be required for effective "computerizing" of PERT data. This is because of the dynamic quality of PERT Management Systems. For example, input data tends not to be as "clean" as in the case of established business data-processing systems. Networks need to be validated or checked before input to the computer, and as we have seen, these networks are constantly changing. In addition, since PERT Management Systems are still in an evolutionary stage, specific computer programs in this field are constantly being revised.

7. Serving as the *master programming* function for the organization. If explicit multiproject PERT techniques are being used, as mentioned in Chapter 3, this function will almost

necessarily fall within the responsibility of the central PERT staff. In addition, as PERT Management Systems begin to be applied across the board in any organization, aggregate resource planning activities, such as projection of total manpower requirements, expenditure rates, facility and capital requirements, can be more directly coupled to detailed PERT analyses, and thus become more realistic and current at any given time.

For these reasons, as the application of PERT Management Systems increases, there are two opposing trends in connection with the staffing of a central PERT group. On the one hand, as operating personnel throughout the organization begin to build up their own capabilities in PERT techniques through training and experience, the actual implementation and use of the techniques tend to become decentralized. Such a trend is not only desirable, but should be emphasized and fostered by management. The confinement of PERT program planning and analysis to a central staff group, or its use as a "side-loop" operation with no tie-in to operating personnel, represents a serious misuse of the system.

On the other hand, as the use of PERT techniques becomes widespread throughout the organization, there will be need for centralization of some of the specialized PERT functions described above. It is the author's view that, for the reasons described above, in the long run these specialized areas of PERT Management Systems and the functions of aggregate planning will be merged together in order to achieve the greatest benefit for the organization.

The exact organizational placement of the central PERT staff group is not as important as the capability of its personnel. PERT staff groups exercising the responsibilities previously described have been located in all areas of the organization. In program-oriented or matrix organizations, however, they are perhaps most effective in reporting directly to the general management or planning function, because of the across-the-board impact and special characteristics of the technique. It is important to emphasize again that PERT Management Systems are concerned with an *integrated approach* to performance, schedule, and cost parameters and, by their very nature, cross over established functional lines. In addition to cutting across the organizational hierarchy, we have seen that they have impact on established systems in the areas of accounting, scheduling, and product identification and control. Thus, the personnel, and particularly the management of the central PERT staff, should have broad experience and capability in all areas of the business affecting these factors—including the technical area—in addition to a thorough knowledge of the details of PERT Management Systems.

Relationship of PERT to Profits: Introduction

The relationship of PERT Management Systems to profits will be discussed in two general categories. The first category will cover payoffs from the early applications of basic PERT/TIME, CPM, and PERT/COST techniques in terms of case histories on actual profit improvement, cost reduction, or schedule improvement results. In the discussion of this first category, the wide spectrum of basic PERT applications that have already been made in both government-oriented and commercial industries will become apparent.

The second category will cover the impact on profits resulting from the application of a complete, integrated PERT system involving performance, time, and cost factors. In this category the relationship of PERT to profits will be described in connection with *multiple-incentive contracting,* i.e., contracting where specific profit incentives are based upon the factors of performance, time, and cost. This situation is mostly confined to the field of large military and space development programs and, as we shall see, represents a very difficult and demanding requirement. Since the use of multiple-incentive contracting was only instituted on a large scale beginning in 1963, there is very little historical data on its actual results. Nevertheless, it is clear that the policy of the Federal government is to use incentive contracts of this type in place of CPFF (Cost-Plus-Fixed-Fee contracts) on all new development-oriented programs where a firm- or fixed-price arrangement is not feasible. The objective of the government is a reduction of CPFF contracting from the peak of 38 per cent of total contract awards in 1961 to approximately 12 per cent of total procurements by 1965.[2] The difference will be taken up by a shift to incentive-type contracts.

The specifics of the relationship between PERT Management Systems and this important new development will be discussed in a later section. However, it is important to recognize that any organization in the military and space field which is not able to meet the demanding requirements of multiple-incentive contracting is not likely to be the recipient of major government contract awards. Hence, the potential effect on both sales and profits is obvious.

Impact of Basic PERT on Profits

First, let us recite some of the documented results of the use of basic PERT techniques in both government-financed and commercial programs. In April, 1963, the Bureau of the Budget published a report entitled *Cost Reduction through Better Management in the Federal Government*.[3] In this report, the following cases of cost reduction or schedule improvement by the use of basic PERT were cited:

Some Specific Benefits

The principal value of PERT, both time and cost, is as an aid to improved management. It helps the manager by providing timely information which assists him in making important decisions. The manager himself must take the responsibility and credit for making decisions. Nevertheless, some illustrations of how PERT has been strikingly useful to managers are included below:

NAVY—Has reported an early demonstration of the benefits of PERT/COST. A contractor reported an $850,000 cost overrun and requested additional funding. By use of PERT/COST techniques, it was possible to prune out $250,000 of nonessential work and classify $435,000 of the reported overrun as change in contract scope subject to negotiation, in which additional savings might be made.

ARMY—Has found the networking and scheduling aspects of PERT most useful, especially in construction projects. In one typical case, contractor personnel were scheduled to depart shortly for an isolated Pacific Isle to install radar equipment. A routine PERT analysis indicated that installation of the shielding for the radar room was falling behind. The construction contractor was promptly notified to order the shielding and departure of the radar installation personnel was delayed one month, thereby minimizing schedule slippage and preventing an estimated $100,000 of extra expense in paying idle contractor personnel.

AIR FORCE—The scheduling benefits from PERT are illustrated in the C-141 program, the development of a subsonic aircraft. Three contractors all thought they were doing their job in the propulsion area as scheduled and they were complying with the terms of their separate contracts in all respects. When their respective efforts were integrated on an overall network, it became apparent that the propulsion system would be delayed 36 weeks. Network analysis soon discovered the principal problem, that one contractor was waiting for receipt of a production engine from a second contractor before proceeding with design of the engine covering. A metal mockup engine was supplied and constant monitoring of the interdependent effort required by all three contractors reduced the delay from 36 to 8 weeks, representing a substantial reduction in costs.

NASA—PERT was used by the National Aeronautics and Space Administration to help prepare a feasible approach for a manned lunar landing. It was discovered that the critical item, whose delay would case most harm to the project schedule was the acquisition of land for, and construction of, launching sites. This resulted in an early approval to expand the Atlantic Missile Range.

NASA also uses PERT on some of its contracts. In one such case, a major contractor requested overtime authorization on a number of specific tasks. PERT reports permitted the NASA Project Manager to discover that some of the tasks had already been completed and the remainder were in areas where there was no need for rush work. The request was denied.

AEC—Besides using PERT for controlling research and development projects and construction work, the Atomic Energy Commission has applied the technique to other kinds of problems. One such application is at the National Reactor Testing Station in Idaho. Through PERT the shut down times on 2 different test reactors were reduced from 10 to 15 per cent, saving an estimated $3,000 every 4 weeks on one reactor, and $14,500 every 6 weeks on the other. In addition, better management control, improved quality of workmanship, better utilization of manpower, and a reduction in radiation exposure of craftsmen is achieved. Another unique use of PERT was in planning and administering the transfer of the Los Alamos, N. Mex. community from Government to private ownership. Still another unusual use is for the maintenance work on the huge gaseous diffusion plants at Oak Ridge, Tenn.

It should be recognized that the situation of cost reduction may or may not represent actual profit pickups for the industrial contractors involved. In fixed-price or incentive-type arrangements, they are likely to produce a profit gain; in CPFF arrangements, they are not. Nevertheless, the explicit control actions undertaken to improve cost and schedule, as shown by these examples, represent an improvement in the management of such programs. In the long run this improvement in management should improve the profit returns of companies engaged in government-financed work through reduction of overruns and betterment of basic cost positions. As was discussed in Chapter 4 in connection with the objectives of PERT/COST, the reduction of the high levels of overrun experienced in the past should come about not only through the control aspects of PERT, but through more realistic *initial* estimating of costs and schedules by contractors, and recognition of and emphasis on this fact by the government in the award of contracts.

Impact on Commercial Profits

Next we shall turn to some examples of the impact of basic PERT or CPM on purely commercial operations. In an article in the December, 1962, *Operations Research,* J. W. Pocock of the Booz-Allen Applied Research group reported the results of an extensive survey as follows: [4]

> If we arrange the commercial applications covered in this survey by a type grouping, the totals run as follows—giving the percentage of the companies surveyed who used PERT or some similar network system in these various areas:

> | | |
> |---|---|
> | Research and development | 25% |
> | Construction programs | 24 |
> | Programming of computers | 12 |
> | Preparation of bids and proposals | 12 |
> | Maintenance planning | 12 |
> | Installation of computer systems | 8 |
> | Distribution planning | 5 |
> | Cost reduction programs | 5 |
> | Miscellaneous | 4 |

The totals do not add up to 100 per cent, simply because some of the companies use their system in several of these areas.

Thus, we see clearly that a variety of applications is developing which speaks to the point of the universality of this type of programming system. But generalities are always suspect. Let us review the specific returns from a random selection of commercial applications.

Du Pont

Use—Shutdown maintenance of Louisville plant.
Results—Reduced shutdown time by 37 per cent.
　　　—Gained more than 1 million pounds of production.

International Minerals & Chemical

Use—Maintenance of mine hoist requiring shutdown of mine.
Results—27 per cent time reduction.
　　　—$100,000 saved.

Catalytic Construction Company

Use—47 construction projects.

Results—Average time reduction for projects 22 per cent.

—Expediting costs reduced average of 15 per cent.

Sun Maid Raisin Growers

Use—Construction of plant properly timed to growing season.

Results—Time reduction of 25 per cent.

—Estimated savings of $1,000,000.

The potential uses of PERT and similar systems—those uses being considered or advanced by management during the survey —included the following (and consider the variety in this list): securities issues, long-range planning, marketing programs, mergers or acquisition programs, introduction of new products, advertising programs, staffing of plants, installing other management control systems, installing organization plans, book publication—and so it goes.

One of the most interesting applications now being considered is what we may call precrisis planning. This concerns laying out the program of action that a utility would follow when a hurricane hits the North Carolina coast; what does a steel company do when a strike occurs; what does an automobile manufacturer do if its automatic transmission plant burns. These questions can be answered in programs developed as PERT networks, ready to be invoked should the crisis occur. PERT under these circumstances is on a stand-by basis, ready to be used for improved management of the unexpected.

We notice that in these potential uses most are one-time ventures in which a large number of things must be accomplished and must be effectively integrated. For instance, in a total advertising program there are a number of tasks to be completed by the agency, a number by the company, and a number by the suppliers, all to dovetail and come to fruition at a given time. This is a typical task environment where PERT has worked best.

It is interesting to note that Pocock goes on to describe improvements resulting from the use of PERT, as reported by user executives in his survey, in *both* the areas of planning and control. At the same time he spells out a number of problem areas or "sore spots" which can lead to unprofitable application of the technique:

1. *PERT Is a Management Responsibility.* As a fairly new technique PERT requires more management attention than well-known and tried techniques. PERT must be considered as a means to an end and management must carry responsibility for, first, the judgment as to the practical feasibility of a PERT application in full understanding of what their management information needs are, and secondly, continual monitoring of the usefulness and practicality of the actual installation—else empires grow, piles of paper work blossom, and requests for additional computer capacity proliferate.

2. *PERT Is No Automatic System.* We do not yet completely understand that PERT is by no means an automatic system or a substitute for management decision. In the original report by the Special Projects Office placing PERT in the public domain it was clearly stated at the outset that judgment, human judgment, was at the source of all that PERT could ever provide and that all that PERT could ever provide was output to aid further human judgment.

3. *PERT Often Clashes with Traditional Organization Patterns.* A third major sore spot arising from PERT applications is that PERT cuts across functional, organizational, and company lines. It treats a project as an integrated program and thus departs from traditional, long-standing organizational patterns. It spotlights the nonperformer who formerly was able to hide in his functional fortress. It stipulates coordination and cooperation, cutting across lines of authority at lower levels in a manner which may well be obnoxious to higher management executives who are accustomed through long tradition to running their show successfully as they see fit. The basic trend and pressure comes from the evolution of our new, project-oriented management patterns in industry as our projects become larger and more complex. PERT is simply the instrument which has most clearly exposed this sore spot and triggered the reaction.

4. *Learning to Use a Dynamic Control System.* Management

reaction to the dynamic nature of planning and control, as required under PERT, is that of the man moving from the comfort of an established pattern to the apprehension of the unfamiliar. As individuals, executives, and supervisors have long been trained in static techniques for planning and control information reporting. Their familiarity with these techniques is great, and their success with these methods is unquestioned. Now comes PERT with its opportunity for dynamic planning and control, its continual probing of the future and evaluation of alternative courses of action, its feedback cycle, and its constant change.

5. *The Problem of Poor Applications.* A fifth very sore spot concerns practical application. Our integration with existing management control systems has often been poor. The PERT technique is another management tool and can become an important management tool. But it must be considered in its application in the light of the other management procedures and systems existing. It must be so installed that it makes full use of the inputs and cross-overs from these other systems, and so that its output may be interpreted in relation to the outputs of these other systems to management.

The five areas covered by Pocock above have been treated elsewhere in this book, particularly in Chapter 3, along with other problems of implementation. They are cited here because they represent an excellent summary of some problem areas which, if not understood and resolved by management, will tend to minimize the possibility of any payoffs with the technique.

In Chapters 2 and 4 we discussed the costs of implementing PERT/TIME and PERT/COST, respectively, as a percentage of total program cost. It should be clear that these costs can only be offset by the proper application of PERT Management Systems, including overcoming the problems described above. If PERT is simply treated as a required additional management system, and not actually used by operating-level supervision, it will add to costs, fail to produce any payoffs, and thus *reduce profits, not improve them.* On the other hand, when properly applied, it can yield results of the kind cited in the previous case histories.

Impact on Multiple-incentive Contracting

We now turn to one of the most complex aspects of the relation of PERT Management Systems to profits—namely, the problem of multiple-incentive contracting. As we have seen in Chapter 1, in order to improve total government-industry performance on complex weapons and space development programs, the Department of Defense introduced some new procurement practices in the period 1962 to 1963. These new practices include:

1. Better initial system or program definition
2. New cost estimating and scheduling techniques prior to the system development stage, i.e., PERT/TIME and PERT/COST
3. New program of Contractor Performance Evaluation, based on system definition and PERT/COST
4. Multiple-incentive contracting approaches to industry during the acquisition phase

In the last-named of these approaches, multiple-incentive contracting, an attempt is made to relate profits to the uncertainties and risks associated with achieving performance, time, and cost goals in large-scale development programs.

The concept of this type of incentive contracting is not entirely new. In 1908 the Signal Corps contracted for a flying machine which was to have a target speed of 40 miles per hour. The contract stipulated that the target price would increase or decrease 40 per cent for each 4 miles per hour increase or decrease from the target speed.[5] In recent times the basic philosophy behind this type of incentive contracting has been restated. The philosophy is that contractors who set realistic targets of performance, time, and cost, and actually achieve all three in the execution of a contract, should receive *target profits*.

Those contractors who better performance, time, and cost targets should receive higher-than-average profits; and those who do not should receive lower profits, including possibly even negative profits or losses.

Structure of Multiple-incentive Contracts

The structuring of a multiple-incentive contract refers initially to the "profit weighting" which is placed by the government on the three basic factors of performance, time, and cost, and the amount of "profit swing" which is allocated to each of these factors. Table 8 shows a simplified illustration of the initial structuring of a multiple-incentive contract. Here a target cost of $100 million has been established for the program. *A target fee or profit,* based upon 8 per cent of target cost, has also been established. The level of the target fee itself is a matter of some complexity, being determined by a new procedure called the *Weighted Guidelines method.* This procedure generally results in higher target fees when internal engineering and manufacturing labor is involved in the contract, and lower target fees when there is a high proportion of outside purchased material and subcontracting. After a target fee has been established, based upon the relative mix of these kinds of cost elements, it can be adjusted further for such factors as "contractor assumption of total cost risk" and "record of contractor's performance." [6]

In the example shown in Table 8, after the target fee has been established, it has also been decided that a *fee swing* of from 2 per cent to 14 per cent, or a total of 12 per cent, will be available to the contractor. In CPIF, or Cost-Plus-Incentive-Fee contracts, the statutory limits for this total profit swing are 0 per cent and 15 per cent, respectively. In FPI, or Fixed-Price-Incentive contracts, there are no *statutory* limitations to the range of profit swing, although the contract stipulates a maximum or ceiling price the government will pay. Thus, if the contractor's costs exceed this maximum price, he will experience a negative profit, or a loss. Conversely, there is no statutory upper limit to the amount of profit the contractor can make, such as 15 per cent, although there may be certain administrative practices which would ultimately make the contract subject to a renegotiation board review.

In the example shown in Table 8, it has also been decided that the factor of performance will be weighted at 50 per cent for this particular program, and that the factors of time and cost will each be weighted 25 per cent. As can be seen in the

TABLE 8. A TYPICAL MULTIPLE-INCENTIVE PLAN

Cost-Fee Structure (Amounts assumed for illustrative purposes)	*Millions $*
Target cost	100.0
Target fee	8.0 (8%)
Maximum fee	14.0 (14%)
Minimum fee	2.0 (2%)

Target-incentive Factors	
System performance (profit swing 6%)	½
Costs incurred (profit swing 3%)	¼
Time performance objectives (profit swing 3%)	¼
Total profit swing (12%)	

table, this results in a profit swing of 6 per cent for performance and 3 per cent each for time and cost, which adds up to the total swing of 12 per cent.

It should be emphasized that, in the early phase of a weapons acquisition program, the individual weighing factors for performance, time, and cost may vary considerably, depending on national urgency, state-of-the-art considerations, etc. Generally speaking, however, the highest priority is assigned to performance, followed by time and cost, in that order, with the performance factor receiving more than 50 per cent of the total profit swing. Later, in the production phase, this order of priority may be reversed after performance has been demonstrated by means of a prototype test.

Performance-incentive Structuring

The next step that will be discussed in connection with structuring a multiple-incentive contract is the determination of
what specific factor or factors of performance will be used in
determining performance incentives. This is a complex task in
itself, since these factors must be chosen carefully in order that
they be both representative of the desired results of the program and also quantifiable and measurable at the end of the
development phase. Thus, a *number* of performance factors
may be chosen, such as range, accuracy, weight, and reliability.
The actual target figure for these factors may be established
at the *systems level,* or if the performance factor is difficult to
measure at this level, at the *end item level,* or both. It will be
recalled from Chapter 5 that these performance factors were
the very ones that were studied during systems analysis; that
they themselves were "traded off" against each other during the
process of systems analysis; and that, at the end of the Systems
Definition phase, such overall performance factors were trans-
lated into end item performance specifications. In the case of
large programs, this translation process must be carried out
with not only the internal operating organization but with all
major subcontractors.

Thus, if a thorough Systems Definition effort has been carried
out, as is generally done in the Project Definition phase, the
difficult task of selecting performance factors and establishing
target figures for them is considerably alleviated. For the purpose of "incentivizing," it is desirable to keep the number of
performance factors at a minimum; however, to incentivize a
complex system properly up to a dozen factors may be selected.
Cases of as many as twenty performance factors are known to
have been negotiated in such multiple-incentive contracts. It
should be remembered that within the total performance area,
not only will individual weights have to be assigned for each
of these factors, but data on the *range of uncertainty* around the

targets for each of these performance factors will have to be developed. Clearly, the results and quality of the systems and preliminary design engineering effort carried out during the Project Definition phase will have an important bearing on the profitability of any contract calling for such performance incentives! In fact, it is difficult to visualize how performance incentives which have any real meaning or logic can be developed until the completion of such a thorough Systems Definition effort. It is also clear that engineering personnel who are not ordinarily directly concerned or motivated in the profit area must be trained to meet these new requirements.

In addition to this detailed analysis by the contractor, the government may specify limits on the specific performance factors which have been chosen, in terms of their acceptability in ultimate operation. Examples of this might be a minimum acceptable range or reliability of the system, such as a missile range of 3,000 miles, or an overall probability of successful firing of 0.995. Such limits may or may not have been part of the original basic performance requirements of the system. In addition, they may represent a wide range or an extremely narrow range, depending on the factors involved. After the targets for specific performance factors (along with their outer limits) and weights relating to the total profit swing for performance have been established, it is possible to draw up a number of "profit-performance" trade-off curves. A highly simplified illustration using one performance factor only is shown in the top portion of Figure 54. With a large number of performance factors, a point system can be devised which will allow for single-curve representation of performance versus profit, as shown in the lower portion of Figure 54.

Cost-incentive Structuring

Incentive contracting based upon cost alone has been more widely used than multiple-incentive contracting. Here the problem of structuring is easier to handle than is the case with

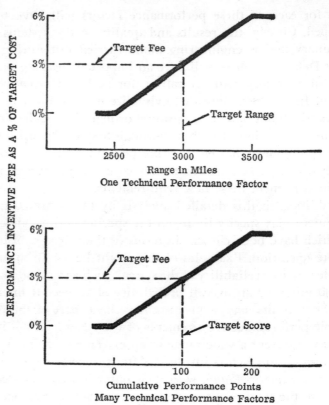

Fig. 54. Illustration of performance-fee structures.

performance incentives, although it has its own individual problems. We shall first discuss a contract based solely upon a simple cost-incentive feature, such as shown in the top portion of Figure 55.

Here we see a target cost of $10 million for an entire program, and a target fee of 6 per cent or $600,000 with a fee swing from 2 per cent to 10 per cent, or $200,000 to $1,000,000. These outer limits of fee occur at program costs of $12 million and $8 million, respectively. It will be noted that from this data three "cost-fee" points can be plotted in Figure 55, and a single straight line drawn that passes through all three points. Such a line is called a *sharing line,* and its slope is called the *sharing formula* for this particular cost-incentive arrangement. Note that if costs are under target by $1 million, the fee rises by $200,000; i.e., the contractor shares 20 per cent for every dollar he saves. Conversely, if costs increase by 1 million above target,

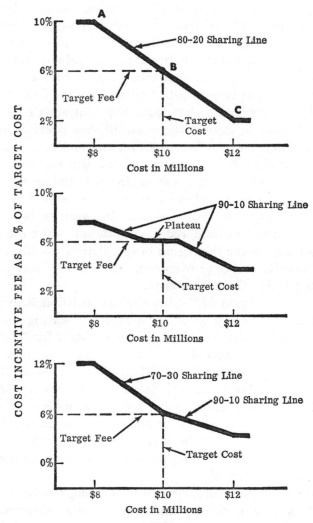

Fig. 55. Illustration of cost-incentive fee structures for an entire program.

the fee goes down by $200,000. The effect of this is that the customer is paying only 80 per cent of the increase in cost. Thus the sharing line in Figure 55 represents the fairly common "80-20" sharing formula, which in this case remains constant throughout the range of the fee-cost relationship.

It is generally assumed that the sharing formula should be related to the degree of risk or uncertainty involved in a particular contract. Thus, if there is uncertainty about the validity of the target cost, and it is believed that actual costs can be substantially lower or higher than this target figure, a *90-10 sharing formula* might be established rather than the 80-20 formula. This situation would reflect both the contractor's desire for greater protection against the possibility of overrun and the customer's desire to pay less profit on any underrun condition. In this situation the two parties might also construct a "fee plateau" around the target cost, as shown in the center portion of Figure 55. The introduction of a plateau would reflect the belief that small underruns or overruns were to be expected and were not to be considered too significant, while the steeper sharing lines outside the region of the plateau would provide a higher penalty for large overruns, and a strong incentive for incurring a significant underrun.

Still another aspect of the uncertainty situation is in the setting of the target cost level. This aspect of setting the target fee will also be related to the adjustment factor for "contractor assumption of total cost risk," which was mentioned previously in the discussion on the Weighted Guidelines method. Suppose a contractor believes that the target cost he has developed is tight. He will then seek a greater fee for an underrun situation as well as greater protection for an overrun condition. This situation is reflected in the "broken" sharing line at the bottom of Figure 55, where the sharing formula is 70-30 above the target fee and 90-10 below it.

Thus we see that cost-incentive structuring can be used with a good deal of flexibility and can become correspondingly complex, depending upon the uncertainty of the target cost and the range and shape of the probability curve of cost over-run and underrun around it. While these concepts are relatively easy to set forth, actual implementation, i.e., the development of meaningful cost data to sustain such a structure, is a much more difficult matter. We shall return to this problem in connection with the introduction of the uncertainty factor into PERT/COST, and the combining of all three factors, i.e., performance, time, and cost, in true multiple-incentive contracting.

Schedule-incentive Structuring

Schedule-incentive structuring has its own unique problems, and again we shall initially treat it as a single-incentive feature. The use of PERT/TIME is particularly significant in establishing schedule incentives, since events on a PERT network must be carefully defined, and are therefore susceptible to a determination of actual status. In the simplest case, the entire schedule-incentive fee might be based upon meeting the delivery date for a final event shown on a PERT network, such as completion of an initial prototype test. In this case, as can be seen in the top portion of Figure 56, the fee might be related to the number of months behind or ahead of scheduled delivery date. But there are other important delivery dates in any PERT network, such as events for additional protoypes or documentation items. The question then becomes: To what extent should other deliverable items, shown as terminating events on the PERT network, be included in the schedule incentive formula? In addition, to what extent should key or milestone events leading up to the terminating event or events be included in the schedule-incentive formula? Certainly, PERT analysis tells us that, if key events lying along the critical-path areas are missed, the terminating event(s) will slip by a corresponding amount, unless management action can effect speedup of downstream activities in the program.

As in the case of performance incentives, a weighting approach is likely to be used, with the major terminating event or events being given larger weights, and milestone events leading up to them being assigned small weights. In addition, the months behind-or-ahead-of-schedule principle used for the single-ter-

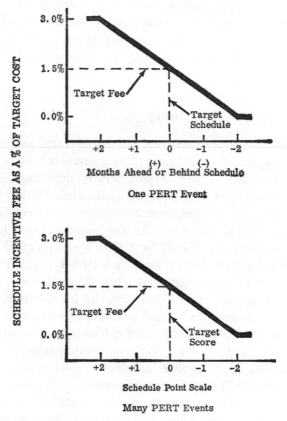

Fig. 56. Illustration of schedule-incentive fee structures.

minating event situation would no longer apply. One alternative in this case is to establish an index based upon the sum of all the weighting figures assigned to particular events. If all events are achieved on schedule, the maximum fee is obtained; if none are achieved on schedule, the minimum fee results. In between these two extremes, that amount of fee paid is dependent upon the score achieved, i.e., the events completed on schedule times their relative weights. An example of the use of such a fee-index relationship is shown in the lower portion of Figure 56.

It should be emphasized that, in using this particular approach, schedule performance becomes a Go-No-Go situation; i.e., in order to obtain the incentive fee on any particular event the completion date must be met exactly as scheduled. In order to bring time uncertainty into the picture, it would be desirable to have a fee versus time plateau around each selected schedule-incentive event. As we have seen, standard PERT/TIME analysis can be used in establishing such plateaus in terms of both schedule targets and range of schedule uncertainty around them. For analysis in this situation, we would want to retain the cumulative variance figure described in Chapter 2. Thus the relationship of PERT/TIME to the schedule aspects of multiple-incentive contracting is clear and, if properly applied, should provide the contractor with a powerful analytical tool for developing a meaningful schedule-incentive structure.

It should be pointed out, however, that in the area of schedule there is often little desire on the part of the customer or government to reward contractors for achieving schedule performance *ahead* of a given target date. Indeed, the incentive generally offered has been purely a negative one, i.e., a penalty only for late performance against schedule dates. This approach is sometimes reflected in a "liquidated damages" provision in the contract, i.e., a clause in which the contractor is required to pay the customer a certain dollar figure for each day of slippage against a scheduled delivery date. When schedule uncertainties are actually present, however, a true incentive approach must offer *both* rewards for meeting or beating schedule dates as well as penalties for being late, within a reasonable range or plateau area.

Combination of Three Incentive Factors

In the preceding sections, the difficulties and problems inherent in handling each of the incentive factors of performance, cost, and time have been discussed. Now we must view the situation where *all three factors* are operating simultaneously, as they do in any program with a high development content. Thus, multiple-incentive contracting takes recognition of the fact that all three fee structures—performance, cost, time—are interrelated. This situation is illustrated in Figure 57, where all three incentive-fee structures are shown in simplified forms, but operating simultaneously. Multiple-incentive contracting represents the "capstone" of the integration of performance, time, and cost factors, which has been developed throughout this book. In addition it is of direct interest to top management since it represents an explicit tie-in of profits to this basic concept.

It is clear that the curves in Figure 57 should be structured or balanced in such a way as to motivate the contractor to achieve the important goals of the program. We have discussed the difficulties of achieving this objective in the case of any one of the incentives treated individually. Therefore it should be apparent that an explicit approach to structuring all three factors simultaneously is an extremely complex problem. For example, in Figure 57, performance targets are likely to be surpassed only by an increase in time and cost, or both. Costs cannot generally be reduced below target without affecting performance or schedules. Shortening the schedule will undoubtedly have impact on both performance and cost. The question the contractor must ask himself as he develops or negotiates such a multiple-incentive fee structure is this: What is the numerical value of these effects? How much do cost and time increase with an increase in performance for any one technical parameter, and what is the uncertainty or probability of achieving this improved performance level? On the government or customer's side, the same kinds of questions exist. However, the customer's problem is now one of *value;* i.e., what is the *value* to the government for a given increase in performance? This concept of value is very similar to the one discussed at the end of Chapter 4 and in Chapter 5. The value of increase in performance is related to

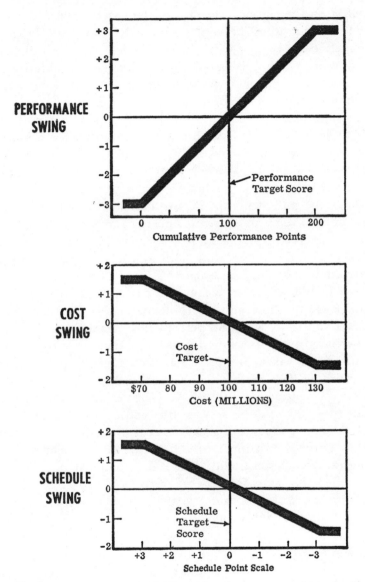

Fig. 57. Illustration of multiple-incentive factors operating simultaneously.

its effect on the cost-effectiveness of the system, difficult as this may be to determine. Thus, what is involved in multiple-incentive contracting is an "*n*-dimensional model," in which the contractor seeks to establish a structure which will maximize his profits and the customer seeks to maximize the value of the system minus its costs if these can be determined.

It should also be evident from this discussion that it is possible to develop a very large number of incentive-fee combinations under the multiple-incentive structuring. The total number of possible profit plans is a function not only of the number of technical, cost and schedule parameters chosen, but also of the shape and structure of the individual fee-relationship lines. In order to implement multiple-incentive contracting with any degree of practicality, it becomes necessary to reduce the total incentive-fee combinations to a small number and yet satisfy the objectives of both parties.

To gain a better appreciation of the complexity of this situation, let us first examine the problem in only two dimensions, i.e., cost and time, with the performance factor fixed. We will further simplify the problem by assuming that a cost-time curve of the type shown in Figure 58 has been established for an entire program. The reader will recognize that such a cost-time curve, representing the sum of total direct and nondirect costs versus time, is the same as was discussed at the end of Chapter 4. Also for purposes of simplification, we will omit the penalty-cost curve shown in Figure 46 of Chapter 4 because of the very great difficulty of quantifying it in system programs. It will be recalled that this penalty-cost curve represents the reverse or reciprocal version of *value* to the customer. Hence, the following discussion will center around the problem of multiple-incentive structuring from the contractor's point of view.

In addition to the cost-time curve, let us add a third dimension to Figure 58, which contains a series of curves representing *lines of constant fee*. Any one of these lines represents the fee that would result if the product were developed to meet a given performance specification within combinations of time and cost shown in the two-dimensional space of Figure 58. Conceptually, the optimum time-cost point for a maximum fee (point *A*) can be found by inspection of the simplified representation of the model shown in Figure 58. In fact, however, with more than one schedule parameter and with nonlinearities

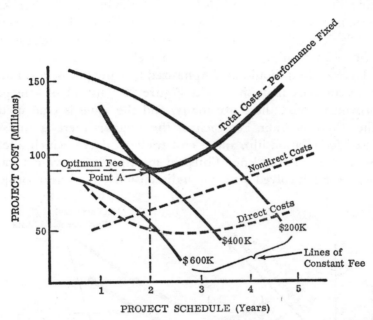

Fig. 58. Illustration of multiple-incentive fee optimization (cost and time only).

in both the cost-time and the fee sharing-line curves, the problem is an *n*-dimensional one and much more complex than represented in Figure 58.

Now let us remove the restriction that performance is constant, and represent increasing levels of performance as another new dimension, as illustrated in Figure 59. Here again we are treating the case of an entire program. Figure 59 is comprised of a set of cost-time curves, representing *lines of constant performance,* with the level of performance increasing away from the origin. Target cost, target schedule, and target performance in this simplified illustration intersect at point *B*. Around point *B* there is a three-dimensional space which represents the area in which the contract can be performed; i.e., this is the area determined by contract negotiations with respect to the outer limitations on time, cost, and performance. In theory, leaving aside the matter of *probability* of achieving the higher performance level shown in Figure 59, we could introduce the fourth dimension of fee, and find an optimum time-cost-performance-fee point, i.e., one which yields maximum profit.

Here again it should be emphasized that the problem is much more complex than shown in Figure 59. Instead of one performance factor, there are many, and the same is true in the schedule dimension. For each of these factors there is an associated fee relationship, and a cost trade-off curve, which affects the cost-fee sharing line. Thus, in multiple-incentive contracting we are involved with an *n*-dimensional nonlinear project

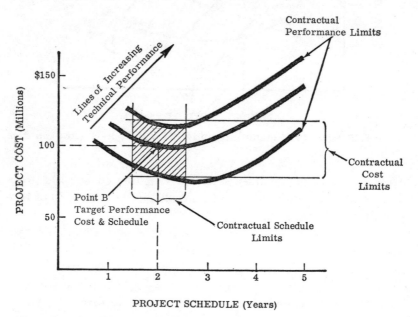

FIG. 59. Illustration of multiple-incentive program performance, time, and cost operating space.

performance space which is exceedingly complex. The theoretical tools to handle this problem are available in nonlinear or dynamic programing techniques. In practice, the possibility of obtaining data to define all the relationships within this n-dimensional nonlinear space (leaving aside any consideration of its accuracy) is extremely doubtful.

PERT Systems and Multiple-incentive Contracting

How, then, can the multiple-incentive contract be structured in any meaningful way, i.e., based upon *some* explicit data on the complex relationships involved? Furthermore, assuming it is meaningfully structured initially, how can the program be controlled so as to yield the desired results of maximum profit for the contractor? How will changes or redirection of the program be handled? If multiple-incentive contracting is to achieve its objectives, it must be related to the *control* aspects of program management; i.e., the performance-time-cost-fee curves must be relatable to the individual program tasks which affect them.

These are very difficult questions to answer in any complete sense. However, it is the author's view that approximate or pragmatic approaches can be found in the methodology of Systems Definition, PERT/TIME, PERT/COST, and Configuration Management, as described in Chapter 5 of this book. However, to do so, the principle of an explicit predictive approach to uncertainty, as is found in PERT/TIME, will have to be preserved in the Systems Definition and PERT/COST aspects of the methodology.

The problem can be stated as follows: For a given technical parameter chosen in multiple-incentive contracting, what is the predicted *range of technical uncertainty* around the target performance specification, and what are the explicit cost and time trade-off relationships associated with it?

It will be recalled that, at the end of the Systems or Project Definition phases, a base-line system configuration was established which represented the best combination for meeting system performance requirements. Associated with this base-line configuration were a set of end item performance specifications, which were related to the Work Breakdown Structure, and against which PERT/TIME networks and PERT/COST Work Packages were developed.

On those performance parameters which have been chosen for multiple-incentive contracting (and they will often be the same ones used in the original systems analysis), we must ask the systems engineer to state a predicted range of technical uncertainty. The major factor affecting this range of uncertainty is what is achievable within the state of the art or the expected state of the art. In addition, there are restraints, generally in the form of lower or cutoff limitations, imposed by the customer. The final established range for any given technical parameter at the system level must be carried down to the affected end item level, or it may have been developed upward from the end item level.

Next cost and time trade-offs must be developed in relation to the established range for each chosen technical parameter. If there are any affected end items on the Work Breakdown Structure which have not been, or cannot be, defined by a thorough process of Systems Definition, gross estimates of technical uncertainty, of the maximum-minimum variety, will have to be made. Associated with these figures will be estimated or "guesstimated" maximum-minimum cost and time figures. These latter data may be obtained from aggregate cost modeling or cost estimating relationship data used, along with time data, in the earlier phases of the Systems Definition process. However, when a thorough Program Definition effort is undertaken, it is presumed that the number of end items on the Work Breakdown Structure which fall into this gross category will be at a minimum.

For all the remaining end items, i.e., those on which a specific technical range around the performance specification target has been established, we may carry out additional analysis on the basic PERT/COST network. It will be recalled that the basic PERT/COST network was developed on the assumption of target performance factors for each End Item Subdivision. Thus we can develop changes or alternatives to the basic PERT/COST network, which should give cost and time data for at least the lower and upper performance points (as well as for the target performance point).

How can this be done? Certainly the entire PERT/COST network for a given end item is not affected, just as all the performance factors chosen for incentive purposes do not necessarily affect the cost-time structure of the entire program. Using the PERT/COST network as a basic framework, we can *isolate* those activities and/or Work Packages which have an effect, or at least the largest effect, upon the particular technical performance parameter involved. (In some cases, we may have to alter the Work Package structure.) For instance, if we are concerned with the reliability of a particular end item, as expressed in terms of its mean-time-between-failure figure (which has been apportioned down to it from the systems level), we can isolate those activities or Work Packages on the network which have the largest impact on the reliability outcome of this end item. For example, in a typical electronics program, these are generally circuit development activities involving critical components, not mechanical items. In addition, we may wish to examine certain testing and redesign activities in connection with developing alternative time-cost data for different levels of technical performance.

Having isolated the activities or Work Packages which have the largest effect on the technical parameter we are considering, how should we go about estimating alternative costs and times for them?

Before going on to this discussion, let us return to a basic assumption of the PERT technique. This assumption is that, for an event to be considered complete, it must have been completed "successfully" against the performance or task objectives of the activity (or activities) leading up to it. In other words, the completion of an event in PERT implies a 1.0 probability, or at least a very high probability, of successful completion for a particular task objective. (It should be remarked parenthetically that H. Eisner has considered the case where the probability of completing an event is low, and alternative "either-or" paths and objectives are opened up.[7]) In this discussion, however, we will maintain the original PERT concept that all paths must be traversed, but we will also ask this question: What changes in PERT/COST network activities will be required to achieve alternative performance levels to within 1.0 probability or close to it?

Another feature of basic PERT must also be emphasized at this point. It will be recalled in PERT/TIME that three-time estimates were made which reflected the time uncertainty involved in achieving a given task objective, assuming a constant level of resources. In essence this time uncertainty also represented a range of cost uncertainty, the extreme value of which (i.e., cost at the pessimistic time estimate) represented the "pad" or "cost contingency" factor needed to perform a given activity successfully. In the DOD approach to basic PERT/COST, this time uncertainty and associated cost uncertainty were dropped in connection with initial implementation of the system. To the extent that costs revealed in the DOD PERT/COST system do not reflect this pad or contingency factor, we may wish to reexamine three-time estimates in the analysis of particular Work Packages which are connected with multiple-incentive performance parameters. Such an approach is likely to be particularly significant on testing activities or on any other activities which have a significant three-way time, and therefore cost, spread. The reason for this approach is that if we are going to isolate costs for meeting a particular performance parameter, and these costs are explicitly tied to incentive profits, we may wish to examine the worst or most pessimistic case if it is a significantly large one.

Now, going on to the method of determining cost and time for alternative performance levels, we can develop specific incremental activities or Work Packages on the network, such as "first redesign and test," "second redesign and test," etc., to achieve a higher level of performance. Conversely, such activities or Work Packages can be deleted, along with others in the original basic PERT/COST network, to reflect a lower level of performance.

An important point to emphasize in analyzing the case of increased performance is that such activities can be added in either *series or parallel* on the network. This situation is illustrated in Figure 60. If added *in series,* they are likely to be less costly because they build upon prior knowledge obtained in the development program. Therefore the series approach should be used whenever the activities involved are not on the critical path. If, on the other hand, the incremental activities we are concerned with lie on the critical path, they will undoubtedly have impact on a schedule-incentive event, and may produce an untenable schedule-fee offset, as well as program slippage. The solution in this case is to place such incremental activities *in parallel* on the network—the backup approach if you will. The use of parallel or backup activities will significantly enhance the probability of achieving a higher performance level without any increase in time. However, the effect on cost will generally be higher than the series approach because the full cost of redundant or parallel design approaches is involved. Note that here we have described one of the typical "nonlinearities" in the relationship between performance, time, and cost factors, but one that at least can be treated explicitly when using the PERT/COST network as a basic framework of analysis.

With such an approach to incremental analysis of a well-developed PERT/COST network, explicit data on the relationship of trade-off curves for particular performance parameters can be obtained. A great deal of skill and judgment will be required on the part of the analyst and engineering personnel involved, but perhaps not too much more than is required in developing an initial basic PERT/COST network. As we

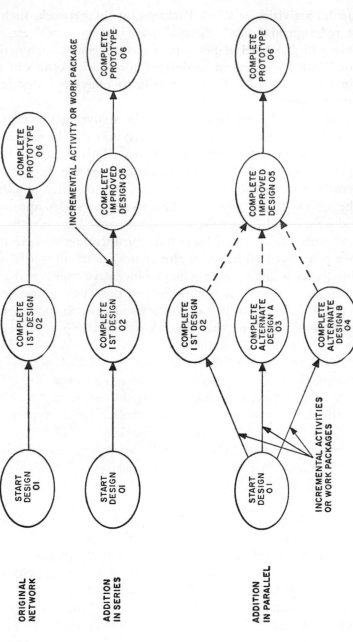

Fig. 60. Illustration of series and parallel approaches for incremental activities or Work Packages.

ORIGINAL NETWORK

START DESIGN 01 → COMPLETE 1 ST DESIGN 02 → COMPLETE PROTOTYPE 06

ADDITION IN SERIES

START DESIGN 01 → COMPLETE 1 ST DESIGN 02 → COMPLETE IMPROVED DESIGN 05 → COMPLETE PROTOTYPE 06

INCREMENTAL ACTIVITY OR WORK PACKAGE

ADDITION IN PARALLEL

START DESIGN 01 → COMPLETE 1 ST DESIGN 02
START DESIGN 01 → COMPLETE ALTERNATE DESIGN A 03
START DESIGN 01 → COMPLETE ALTERNATE DESIGN B 04
→ COMPLETE IMPROVED DESIGN 05 → COMPLETE PROTOTYPE 06

INCREMENTAL ACTIVITIES OR WORK PACKAGES

194

have seen, during the process of developing alternative activities or Work Packages, the analyst will be making internal time, cost, and performance trade-offs. These trade-offs must be made with a view to the overall fee weights assigned to the factors of performance, time, and cost. In addition, other aspects of the multiple-incentive structuring problem, such as the shape of sharing-line curves and the sharing formula, must be kept in mind.

With the methodology of Systems Definition leading into the PERT/COST network as a basic starting point, the analyst should be able to bring out the time and cost relationships associated with particular performance parameters. As has been previously mentioned, he will not be concerned with all activities or Work Packages in the program network, but only with those affecting technical parameters which have been chosen for incentive purposes. This approach should tend to reduce the effort on what otherwise might be an exceedingly difficult task. The cost data which are obtained against various technical parameters may be aggregated and applied to the total cost range of the program in order to reduce the complexity of the incentive structure actually described in the contract. It may or may not be possible to aggregate or synthesize time data on a comparable basis, depending on the schedule events chosen for incentive purposes. However, the contractor will certainly wish to retain his detailed analysis on all technical parameters for the purposes of both negotiation and measuring the effect of program changes. Indeed, if the contractor performs well against the contract, he may wish to have this detailed documentation available in order to sustain higher-than-average profits in any renegotiation proceeding.

As the contract is actually carried out, program redirection and changes will undoubtedly occur. The system for monitoring these changes by means of the Configuration Management function, and the determination of their impact on performance, time, and cost by means of an integrated management system, have been described in Chapter 5. Suffice it to say that significant changes will undoubtedly affect the incentive-fee structure and therefore must be reanalyzed by the contractor. For example, if a redirection of the program calls for a change in performance requirements, but no schedule relief is allowed, the contractor will need to examine the cost of accelerating or crashing PERT/COST activities associated with the particular performance parameters involved. A "reverse" type of analysis would be made if the program were stretched out in time. The basic framework for doing this analysis, i.e., the detailed Work Breakdown Structure and the PERT/COST network itself, need not and should not be written into the contract. To do so would inhibit the flexibility of the contractor in managing the program. However, the *effect* of these changes on the incentive-fee structure will have to be handled by the formal contract change notice and negotiation procedures.

It remains to be seen whether multiple-incentive contracting will achieve the objectives for which it was established. It is possible that its objectives will only be achieved if the process of formal Project Definition is successful; i.e., if meaningful Systems Definition and PERT/TIME and PERT/COST analysis is carried out, proper multiple-incentive structures are established, and there are a greatly reduced number of program changes compared to what has been typical in the past. Nevertheless, an established common methodology and reporting system covering all the above areas, as described in this book, properly implemented by industry, with government or the customer requiring only the higher-level output reports of the system, may help to achieve a significant improvement in the management of the complex undertakings of our times. It may also provide the opportunity for increased profits to industry, based upon superior management of the factors of performance, time, and cost in such complex programs.

REFERENCES

1. Phillip Geddes, *The Impact of New Patterns of Management,* based on interview with J. R. Dempsey, President of General Dynamics/Astronautics, *Aerospace Management,* May, 1963, p. 16.
2. Statement of Thomas D. Morris, Assistant Secretary of Defense (Installations & Logistics) before the SubCommittee on Government Operations, House of Representatives, May 23, 1963.
3. *Cost Reduction through Better Management in the Federal Government,* Executive Office of the President, Bureau of the Budget, April, 1963.
4. J. W. Pocock, PERT As an Analytical Aid for Program Planning—Its Payoffs and Problems,"—*Operations Research,* vol. 10, no. 6, pp. 893–904, November–December, 1962.
5. *Incentive Contracting Seminar,* prepared for the National Defense Education Institute by Harbridge House, Inc., 1962, p. 1.
6. Armed Services Procurement Regulation, Revision 2, Par. 3-808 on Profit (Including Fees under Cost Reimbursable Contracts), August 5, 1963.
7. H. Eisner, "A Generalized Network Approach to the Planning and Scheduling of a Research Program," *Operations Research,* vol. 10, no. 1, pp. 115–126, January–February, 1962.

Appendix 1
Simplified Derivation of PERT Equations [*]

We begin with the beta distribution:

$$f(t) = K(t - a)^{\alpha}(b - t)^{\gamma} \qquad (1)$$

Where K, α, and γ are functions of a, m, and b, and a, m, and b are the three-time estimates.

To set the value of this probability density function equal to one, we begin by setting the *range* equal to one, i.e.,

$$b - a = 1 \qquad (2)$$

and rescaling the t scale to a new x scale, i.e.,

$$x = \frac{t - a}{b - a} \qquad (3)$$

For the *modal value m,* we have

$$r = \frac{m - a}{b - a} \qquad (4)$$

[*] Source: PERT Summary Report Phase I, Navy Special Projects Office (U.S. Government Printing Office), 1960.

199

We now establish the functions a and γ:

$$a = m - a \tag{5}$$

$$\gamma = b - m \tag{6}$$

This results in the modal expression

$$r = \frac{a}{a + \gamma} \tag{7}$$

We next introduce the formula for the *variance of x:*

$$\sigma_x^2 = \frac{(a + 1)}{(a + \gamma + 2)^2} \frac{(\gamma + 1)}{(a + \gamma + 3)} \tag{8}$$

We now make the *simplifying assumption* that the standard deviation σ is equal to one-sixth of the range:

$$\sigma = \frac{b - a}{6} = \frac{1}{6} \tag{9}$$

so that

$$\frac{1}{36} = \frac{(a + 1)}{(a + \gamma + 2)^2} \frac{(\gamma + 1)}{(a + \gamma + 3)} \tag{10}$$

Substituting Eq. (7), we have the cubic equation:

$$a^3 + (36r^3 - 36r^2 + 7r)a^2 - 20r^2a - 24r^3 = 0 \tag{11}$$

We next introduce the formula for the *expected value of x:*

$$E(x) = \frac{a + 1}{a + \gamma + 2} \tag{12}$$

With known values for a, m, and b, we can solve for the value of $E_{(t)}$ (or t_e, the PERT expected time) by use of Eqs. (7), (11), (12), and (3). However, this involves solution of a cubic equation, Eq. (11).

Let us plot some values of r [Eq. (7)] versus $E_{(x)}$ [Eq. (12)] using Eq. (11). The plot yields a *straight-line approximation:*

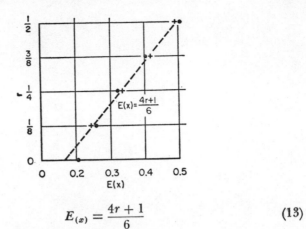

$$E_{(x)} = \frac{4r + 1}{6} \tag{13}$$

Substituting from Eq. (4), and using the expression for $E_{(x)}$

$$E(x) = \frac{t_e - a}{b - a}$$

we get

$$t_e = \frac{a + 4m + b}{6}$$

Appendix 2
Representative Bibliography

AFSC PERT Cost System Description Manual, Air Force Systems Command (SCCS), Washington 25, D.C., May, 1963.

AFSC PERT/TIME Systems Description Manual, Air Force Systems Command (SCCS), Washington 25, D.C., June, 1963.

Army Materiel Command Regulation 11–16, "Planning and Control Techniques for Project Management," vol. II, Hq. Army Materiel Command, Washington, D.C., August, 1963.

Asher, Harold: *Cost-Quantity Relationships in the Airframe Industry,* Project RAND, Report R-291, July 1, 1956.

Avots, Ivars: "The Management Side of PERT," *California Management Review,* June, 1962.

Backer, Frederick, Jr: "A Discussion of Problems Involved in LESS (Least Cost Estimating and Scheduling)," unpublished paper, International Business Machines Corporation, Western Region, Industry Marketing, 3424 Wilshire Blvd., Los Angeles, Calif., 1960.

Bellis, B. N.: *The Requirements for Configuration Management during Concurrency,* Air Force Systems Command Management Conference, Monterey, Calif., May, 1962.

Bobak, E. T.: "The Design, Implementation and Operation of a PERT System on a Space Program," *Aerospace Management,* March, 1963.

Boose, J. A.: *A Non-intuitive Decision-making Method for Configuration of a Complex System,* International Business Machines Corporation, Space Guidance Center, Oswego, N.Y., April, 1963.

Churchman, C. W.: *Introduction to Operations Research,* John Wiley & Sons, Inc., New York, 1957.

Clark, C.: "The Optimum Allocation of Resources among the Activities of a Network," *Journal of Industrial Engineering,* January–February, 1961.

Configuration Management, Air Force Systems Command Manual 375-1, June 1, 1962.

Cost Reduction through Better Management in the Federal Government, Executive Office of the President, Bureau of the Budget, April, 1963.

Critical Path Planning and Scheduling—An Introduction, Mauchly Associates, Fort Washington, Pa., May, 1960.

A Discussion of an Action Planning and Control Technique, International Minerals and Chemical Corporation, Freeport, Tex., August, 1960.

DOD/NASA PERT/COST Guide, U.S. Government Printing Office, Washington, D.C., June, 1962.

Eckman, Donald P.: *Systems Research and Design,* John Wiley & Sons, Inc., New York, 1961.

Fischer, June O.: *PERT/COST with Simulation,* Douglas Aircraft Company, Inc., General Offices, Santa Monica, Calif., October, 1961.

Forrester, J. W.: *Industrial Dynamics,* The M.I.T. Press, Massachusetts Institute of Technology, Cambridge, Mass., 1961.

Freeman, Raoul J.: "A Generalized Network Approach to Project Activity Sequencing," *IRE Transactions on Engineering Management,* September, 1960.

Fulkerson, D. R.: "A Network Flow Computation for Project Cost Curves," *Management Sciences,* vol. 7, pp. 167–178, January, 1961.

Fulkerson, D. R.: "Expected Critical Path Lengths in PERT Networks," RAND Corporation, Memo RM-3075-PR, Santa Monica, Calif., March, 1962.

Goode, Harry H., and Robert E. Machol: *System Engineering,* McGraw-Hill Book Company, Inc., New York, 1957.

Hall, A. D.: *A Methodology for Systems Engineering,* Van Nostrand, Princeton, 1962.

Hitch, C. J.: "Plans, Programs and Budgets in the Department of Defense," *Operations Research,* vol. 11, no. 1, January–February, 1963.

Hower, R. M., and Orth, C. D.: *Manager and Scientists,* Division of Research, Harvard University, Boston, 1963.

The Impact of New Patterns of Management, P. Geddes interview with J. R. Dempsey, President of General Dynamics/Astronautics, *Aerospace Management,* May, 1963.

Incentive Contracting Seminar, prepared for the National Defense Education Institute by Harbridge House, Inc., 1962.

Introduction to PERT, Booz, Allen & Hamilton, Washington 6, D.C., May 16, 1960.

Kast, Fremont E., and James E. Rosenzweig: *Science, Technology and Management*, McGraw-Hill Book Company, Inc., New York, 1963.

Kelly, J. E., Jr.: "Critical Path Planning and Scheduling: Mathematical Basis," *Operations Research*, vol. 9, pp. 296–320. May–June, 1961.

Line of Balance Technology, Navy Department, Office of Naval Material (NAVEXOSP1851 Rev. 4-62), Washington, D.C., April, 1962.

Livingston, J.: "The New Management Elite," *Journal of Armed Forces Management Association*, 1961.

MacCrimmon, K. R., and C. A. Ryavec: *An Analytical Study of the PERT Assumptions*, RAND Corporation, Memo RM-3408-PR, Santa Monica, Calif., December, 1962.

Malcolm, D. G.: "Extensions and Applications of PERT as a System Management Tool," *Operations Research, Inc.*, Silver Springs, Md., March, 1961.

Marshall, A. W., and W. H. Meckling: *Predictability of the Costs, Time, and Success of Development*, RAND Corporation, Report P-1821, December, 1959.

McGee, A. A., and M. D. Markarian: "Optimum Allocation of Research/Engineering Manpower within a Multi-project Organizational Structure," *IRE Transactions on Engineering Management*, vol. EM-9, no. 3, September, 1962.

Miller, Robert W.: "How to Plan and Control with PERT," *Harvard Business Review*, March–April, 1962.

Miller, Robert W.: "Program Cost Uncertainty-Prediction and Control Using PERT Techniques," *M.I.T. Industrial Management Review*, Spring, 1963.

Miner, R. H., and A. Leinwohl: *Polaris PERT/COST System*, '64 *Implementation Plan*, Missile Systems Division, Lockheed M&S Company, Sunnyvale, Calif., 1963.

Mundorff, Geary T., and William Bloom: *Managing a Development Program*, Bureau of Research and Development, FAA, General Precision, Inc., New York, 1960.

Murray, John C.: *Consideration of PERT Assumptions*, Conductron Corporation, Ann Arbor, Mich., 1962.

Norden, P. V., and F. J. O'Reilly: *Life Cycle Method of Project Planning and Control*, International Business Machines Corporation, Data Systems Division, Poughkeepsie, N.Y., 1960.

Packard, K.: "Probabilistic Forecasting of Manpower Requirements," *IRE Transactions on Engineering Management*, vol. EM-9, no. 3, September, 1962.

Pearlman, Jerome: "Engineering Program Planning and Control through the Use of PERT," *IRE Transactions on Engineering Management,* vol. 7, pp. 125–134, 1960.

Peck, M. J. and Scherer, F. M.: *The Weapons Acquisition Process: An Economic Analysis,* Division of Research, Graduate School of Business Administration, Harvard University, Cambridge, Mass., 1962.

PERT—A Dynamic Project Planning and Control Method, International Business Machines Corporation, Data Processing Division, New York, October, 1961.

PERT—Application at LMED, General Electric LMED, Utica, N.Y., 1960.

"PERT/COST Output Reports," Supplement No. 1, *DOD/NASA PERT/ COST Guide,* 1963.

The PERT/COST System, Management Systems Corporation, Cambridge, Mass., December, 1961.

"PERT Guide for Management Use," U.S. Government Printing Office, August, 1963.

"PERT in Perspective," remarks by George E. Fouch, presented to the PERT Instructor's Institute, Air Force Systems Command (SCCS), Washington, D.C., Sept. 24, 1962.

PERT Summary Report Phase I, Navy Special Projects Office (Government Printing Office Catalog No. D217.2: P94/958—25¢), 1960.

PERT Summary Report Phase II, Navy Special Projects Office (Government Printing Office Catalog No. D217.2 P94/958-2—50¢), 1960.

PERT/TIME and PERT/COST, Management Systems for Planning and Control, Spec. MIL P-23189 (A)/(Navy), 1962.

Pettit, J. T.: *A Management Concept for the Defense Industry,* Hughes Aircraft Company, Culver City, Calif., 1961.

PLANNET—A Scheduling Technique for Everyone, Pan American Airways, Guided Missile Range Division, Patrick Air Force Base, Fla., August, 1961.

Program Definition Phase, Hq. Air Force Systems Command, USAF, February, 1963.

Roseboom, J., C. Clark, W. Fazar, and D. Malcolm: "Application of a Technique for Research and Development Program Evaluation," *Operations Research,* vol. 7, no. 5, September–October, 1959.

Statement of Dr. Harold Brown, Director of Defense Research and Engineering, before the Military Operations SubCommittee on Government Operations, May 21, 1963.

Statement of Thomas D. Morris, Assistant Secretary of Defense (Installations & Logistics), before the SubCommittee on Government Operations, House of Representatives, May 23, 1963.

Systems Analysis: Procedures for System Definition, Hq. Ballistic Systems Division, Air Force Systems Command, USAF, June, 1962.

Appendix 3

Glossary of Some Representative Management
Systems Terms*

ABLE—Activity Balance Line Evaluation

A program status measuring forecasting and reporting system. The name derives from the summary of management presentation where accumulative summaries of processes are shown in balance against a "today" line on the time field.

   source: Missile and Space Division
          General Electric Company
          P.O. Box 8555
          Philadelphia 1, Pa.

BUWEPS PERT MILESTONE SYSTEM

By combining advanced management techniques with the full utilization of the computer capability, the system is designed to improve communications for facilitating decision-making process in the Navy-Contractor team endeavor for developing new weapon systems.

---

   * Source: "Management Systems Terminology," PERT Orientation & Training Center, Bolling Air Force Base, Washington, D.C., June, 1963.

source: U.S. Navy Department
Bureau of Naval Weapons
Programs Office
Washington 25, D.C.

COMET—Computer Operated Management Evaluation Technique

Designed for use in planning, scheduling, and monitoring the acquisition of electronic equipments and systems. Represents a unique combination of advanced computer techniques and management methods.

source: U.S. Army Department
Signal Corps Logistics Evaluation Committee
225 S. 18th Street
Philadelphia 3, Pa.

CPA—Cost Planning and Appraisal

A system to assist equipment managers in developing a more effective means of managing cost-type contracts by integrating data on cost, time, and technology.

source: Aeronautical Systems Division
Air Force Systems Command
Wright-Patterson Air Force Base, Ohio

CPM—Critical Path Method

A computer-oriented planning and control method which enables the project manager to see the relationship that each job bears to the project and those which are critical to the on-time completion of the project. It employs a time-oriented network, cost-curve data, and manpower loading techniques. Permits utilization of a normal and a crash estimate of time and cost to reduce program time with minimum cost increase. Devised initially in 1957 by E. I. Du Pont de Nemours & Company and Remington Rand UNIVAC.

source: Mauchly Associates, Inc.
Fort Washington, Pa.

HEPP—Hoffman Evaluation Program and Procedure

An activity-oriented planning and control system tailored especially for research and development work. Presents the following prime elements of a program plan on a single graphic display: work activities, hardware, time allocation of resources, and costs. Frequent updating shows what has happened since the last review period and anticipated departures from the plan.

SOURCE: Military Products Division
Hoffman Electronics Corporation
3740 Grand Avenue
Los Angeles 54, Calif.

ICON—*Integrated Control*

A management information system which is used (1) in the preparation and dollar evaluation of bids and in periodic reevaluation after contract award; (2) for scheduling through PERT techniques including a network reduction algorithm and complete master file maintenance; and (3) for complete data collection and reporting of actual versus planned expenditure of time, dollars, and manpower.

SOURCE: Sylvania Electronic Systems Division
Sylvania Electric Products, Inc.
189 B Street
Needham Heights 94, Mass.

IMPACT—*Integrated Managerial Programming Analysis Control Technique*

Provides progress reporting and GFAE program control through use of a standardized PERT network and an equipment procurement factor data bank. The system includes milestone reporting, procurement document control, item identification, efficiency forecasting, fund commitment and obligation forecasting and GFAE work load forecasting. This system is processed partially by a 7090 computer system and partially through a PCAM system.

SOURCE: Deputy for Equipment Management
GFAE Control Division
Aeronautical Systems Division
Air Force Systems Command
Wright-Patterson Air Force Base, Ohio

LESS—*Least Cost Estimating and Scheduling*

A system for determining the fastest and most economical method of completing a project, using arrow diagramming.

SOURCE: International Business Machines Corporation
Rockville, Md.

LOB—Line of Balance

A production planning system which time-schedules key events necessary for completing an assembly with respect to the delivery dates for the completed system. This information is keyed on bar charts and related to contract schedules against actual delivery. Production plan progress is charted and a line of balance generated to show revised requirements for keeping to schedule. A cost balance is often introduced. Line-of-balance charts can be keyed to various levels of management to suit particular needs.

MPACS—Management Planning and Control System

MPACS is the basic communication of financial and manpower data—budget versus actual—from the accounting or data-collecting agency to the contract-performance-responsible program manager and performing functional manager. It provides data weekly, three working days after the close of the previous week. With the advent of PERT/COST, MPACS was reconstructed to include PERT/COST terminology. It thus serves as the bridge between the detail cost within a Work Package and PERT/COST's summary figure of "actual costs." It also provides the Work Package manager with the inception-to-date expended and committed data so that he can better prepare the PERT/COST Estimating and Updating Form. Uses 1410, 1401, and 704 computers on all government contracts.

SOURCE: Federal Systems Division
International Business Machines Corporation
Rockville, Md.

NASA PERT AND COMPANION COST

Designed as a total management system concept. Integrates the normal existing NASA management and administrative tools and processes into a disciplined planning, control, and reporting instrument for the project manager. The basic theme is that total project management can be achieved only if the three management variables—time, resources, and performance—are managed and manipulated on a common framework which classifies all work elements of the project beginning from the top and shredding out the successive tiers representing systems, subsystems, etc., which make up the project.

SOURCE: Director of Management Reports
Office of Programs
NASA
Washington 25, D.C.

PAAC—Program Analysis Adaptable Control Technique

A method of extracting, analyzing, and summarizing planned and actual data contained in the engineering management information system independent of the existing Work Breakdown Structures used for individual project control purposes. Provides the ability to anticipate the control needs of both customer and program manager, integrate these into the overall reporting system, and then automatically recover the data to support these needs. Uses a Honeywell-800 computer as its central data-processing instrument.

SOURCE: Military Products Group Aeronautical Division
Minneapolis-Honeywell Regulator Company
2600 Ridgeway Road
Minneapolis 40, Minn.

PAR—Project Audit Report

A modified PERT/COST system, based upon the presently used systems within the Burroughs Detroit Division, used to fulfill the need for increased initial planning as well as prompt and accurate reporting techniques. It provides an extremely effective tool for time/cost reporting of projects of any magnitude, affording a documented, logically ordered history of past performance, which, when statistically evaluated and analyzed, will serve in sharpening abilities for future project planning and cost estimating.

SOURCE: Detroit M&E Division
Burroughs Corporation
6071 Second Avenue
Detroit 32, Mich.

PEP—Program Evaluation Procedure

The original Air Force version of PERT.

PERT—Program Evaluation and Review Technique

A management information and control system used in the planning, control and evaluation of progress of a program. It is time-oriented and uses a network to reflect events and activities. The basic system was designed by the Navy for its Polaris program. It is now being used by the Department of Defense, NASA, and other government agencies and industries.

SOURCE: Air Force Systems Command (SCCS)
Andrews Air Force Base
Washington 25, D.C.

PERT II

A version of PERT used by the Ballistic Systems Division, Air Force Systems Command, in the Minuteman program.

SOURCE: Air Force Systems Command (SCCS)
Andrews Air Force Base
Washington 25, D.C.

PERT III

Air Force Systems Command's Standard PERT/TIME Variable System. Integrates PERT (U.S. Navy), as amended and applied by the Aeronautical Systems Division and the Electronic Systems Division, and PERT II (Minuteman), as applied by the Ballistic Systems Division and the Space Systems Division, for uniform application of the PERT/TIME Variable System within the command.

SOURCE: Air Force Systems Command (SCCS)
Andrews Air Force Base
Washington 25, D.C.

PERT IV

Air Force Systems Command's Standard PERT/TIME and Cost Variables System. Integrates PERT III and enumerative cost aspects for uniform application of the PERT/TIME and PERT/COST system within the command.

SOURCE: Air Force Systems Command (SCCS)
Andrews Air Force Base
Washington 25, D.C.

PERT/COST

An extension of the basic PERT/TIME system for the management of complex research and development projects to achieve their technical program objectives. Both cost and schedule are planned and controlled on a common framework or structure, which not only permits more accurate measurement of progress but also enables managers to appraise more realistically the relation of accumulated and projected costs of the program. In addition, it provides insight for alternative courses of action as time and cost are affected. PERT/COST is considered to be in developmental status since it is being tested by the Army, Navy, Air Force, and other organizations.

> SOURCE: Air Force Systems Command (SCCS)
> Andrews Air Force Base
> Washington 25, D.C.

PLANNET—Planning Network

A scheduling technique for planners used in the Guided Missile Range Division of Pan American World Airways. It is visualized scheduling combining bar charts, in series and in parallel, on a time-oriented chart. Similar and supplementary to PERT.

> SOURCE: Guided Missile Range Division
> Pan American World Airways
> Patrick Air Force Base, Fla.

PRISM—Program Reliability Information System for Management

A system for developing new management tools for monitoring and measuring reliability for the Navy Polaris program, as well as improving communications. Uses two unrelated approaches: (1) RMI—*Reliability Maturity Index*, a measure of compliance to the planned reliability activities of development program; (2) RPM—*Reliability Performance Measure*, a prediction of eventual operational reliability of the end item continuously through the development cycle. The methodology employed is an offshoot of the PERT system.

> SOURCE: U.S. Navy Department
> Washington 25, D.C.

RAMPS—Resources Allocation and Multi-Project Scheduling

An automated management technique for making the most of men, materials, and money. Based on Critical Path Method (CPM) and Program Evaluation and Review Technique (PERT). Developed

jointly by CEIR, Inc., and E. I. Du Pont de Nemours & Company.
SOURCE: CEIR, Inc.
　　　　1200 Jefferson Davis Highway
　　　　Arlington 2, Va.

SKED

An integrated computer program for scheduling time and distributing cost. SKED is a standard PERT operation with the addition of a scheduling option based on certain decision rules concerning the allocation of negative and positive slack. Once the slack is allocated, the man-hours and dollars are estimated and the distribution of both evaluated by management. This system is in the development stage.
SOURCE: Finance Section
　　　　Ordnance Department
　　　　General Electric Company
　　　　Pittsfield, Mass.

SPERT—Schedule Performance Evaluation and Review Technique

A program control technique used by the Missile and Space Vehicle Department of General Electric. Based on PERT, except that all events in the network are scheduled with firm dates from the commitment plan, and trend projection and management display methods are utilized from the ABLE system.
SOURCE: Missile and Space Division
　　　　General Electric Company
　　　　P.O. Box 8555
　　　　Philadelphia, Pa.

TOES—Trade-Off Evaluation System

An advanced management tool being developed by AVCO to permit an efficient rational evaluation of technical characteristics, schedules, and cost trade-offs. Aimed at establishing compatibility between PERT and systems analysis, recognizing the conflicting nature of the TCP constraints.
SOURCE: Research and Advanced Development Division
　　　　AVCO
　　　　1701 K Street, N.W.
　　　　Washington, D.C.

TOPS—The Operational PERT System

A generalized PERT system showing only one network. Developed by Aerospace Corporation for use on Air Force Space System Division programs.

    SOURCE: Aerospace Corporation
              2400 E. El Segundo Blvd.
              El Segundo, Calif.

TRACE—Task Reporting and Current Evaluation

A reporting system developed by Ling-Temco-Vought, Inc., for the timely and accurate status reporting of complex programs and the successful management of large and widely dispersed activities. Uses a network of leased lines, data transceivers, and a centralized computing facility.

    SOURCE: Range Systems Division
              Chance Vought Corporation
              P.O. Box 6191
              Dallas, Tex.

WSPACS—Weapon Systems Programming and Control System

A computerized force structure costing technique for broad planning with major emphasis on assessing the impacts of reprogramming actions. It is currently organized as a joint Air Force–Industry effort.

    SOURCE: Aeronautical Systems Division
              Air Force Systems Command
              Wright-Patterson Air Force Base, Ohio

Appendix 4

Glossary of PERT Terminology*

Activity—An element of a program which is represented on a network by an arrow. An activity cannot be started until the event preceding it has occurred. It may represent a process, task, procurement cycle, waiting time, or simply a connection or interdependency between two events on the network.

Activity Slack—See Slack.

Actual Date (T_A)—The calendar date on which an event occurred or an activity was completed.

Beginning Event (BE) (Predecessor Event)—An event which signifies the beginning of one or more activities on a network.

Completion Date—See *Actual Date*.

Condensed Network—A network which represents, with a reduced number of selected events, the relationship of the events to each other and all the significant characteristics of the detailed network. Lines connecting events on a condensed network are not necessarily true, definable work activities, since they are used primarily to portray only the chronological interdependencies and restraints among selected activities.

* SOURCE: Air Force Systems Command, *PERT/TIME System Description Manual*, June, 1963.

Schedule, Cost, and Profit Control with PERT

Constraint—The relationship of an event to a succeeding activity wherein an activity may not start until the event preceding it has occurred. The term "constraint" is also used to indicate the relationship of an activity to a succeeding event wherein an event cannot occur until all activities preceding it have been completed.

Critical Path—That particular sequence of events and activities in a path that has the worst (least algebraic) value slack; therefore, the longest path through the network. Several critical paths may be identified in a network and be ranked in order of their criticality.

Critical Predecessor—The event which immediately precedes the event under consideration and is on the most time-consuming path leading to that event.

Detailed Network—A network which reflects activities at the lowest level of the program breakdown. Detailed networks, while remaining an operating tool of the responsible organization, are related to the program breakdown structure, and their status is reflected in the program management network.

Directed Date for an Event (T_D)—A date for a specific accomplishment formally directed by USAF, DOD, or similar top-level authority.

Earliest Completion Date (S_E)—The earliest calendar date on which a work effort (activity, Work Package, or summary item) can be completed. This date is calculated by:

- Summing the scheduled elapsed times (t_s) for activities on the longest path from the beginning of the program or project to end of the work effort
- Then adding this sum to the calendar start date of the program or project

For distant time effort where scheduled elapsed times (t_s) have not been established, expected elapsed times (t_e) will be used to calculate S_E.

Earliest Expected Date (T_E)—See *Expected Date*.

End Event—That event which signifies the completion of a network.

Ending Event (EE) (Successor)—The event which signifies the completion of one or more activities.

Event—A specific definable accomplishment in a program plan, recognizable at a particular instant in time. Events do not consume time or resources and are normally represented in the network by circles or rectangles.

Event Slack—See *Slack.*

Expected Date (Earliest Expected Date) (T_E)—The calendar date on which an event can be expected to occur. The T_E value for a given event is equal to the sum of the calculated expected elapsed times (t_e) for the activities on the longest path from the beginning of the program to the given event. (This time is transposed to a calendar date by the computer.)

Expected Elapsed Time (t_e)—The elapsed time which an activity is predicted to require. The expected elapsed time is identical to a single-time estimate for the work to be accomplished, or is derived from the calculation of a statistically weighted average time estimate, incorporating the optimistic (a), most likely (m), and pessimistic (b) time estimates for the work to be accomplished:

$$t_e = \frac{a + 4m + b}{6}$$

Interface Event—An event which signals the necessary transfer of responsibility, end items, or information from one detailed network to another. Examples of interface events are the receipt of an item (hardware, drawing, specification), or the release of engineering drawings to manufacturing.

Latest Allowable Date (T_L)—The latest date on which an event can occur without creating an expected delay in the completion of the program. The T_L value for a given event is calculated by subtracting the sum of the *expected* elapsed times (t_e) for the activities on the longest path from the given event to the *end* event of the program from the latest date allowable for completing the program. T_L for the end event in a program is equal to the directed date (T_D) of the program. If a directed date is not specified, $T_L = T_E$ for the end event.

Latest Completion Date (S_L)—The latest calendar date on which a work effort (activity, Work Package, or summary item) can be scheduled for completion without delaying the completion of the program or project. This date is calculated by:
  • Summing the scheduled elapsed times (t_s) for activities on the longest path from the end of the work effort to the end of the program or project

- Then subtracting this sum from the calendar end date of the program or project

For distant time effort where scheduled elapsed times (t_s) have not been established, expected elapsed times (t_e) will be used to calculate S_L.

Level Code—A letter (A through O only) that is associated with an event for shred-out purposes or summarization.

Milestone—Milestones are synonymous with events in a network.

Most Likely Time Estimate (m)—The most realistic estimate of the time an activity might consume. This time would be expected to occur most often if the activity could be repeated numerous times under similar circumstances.

Network—A flow diagram consisting of the activities and events which must be accomplished to reach the program objectives, showing their planned sequences of accomplishment, interdependencies, and interrelationships.

Network Condensing—A process of reducing detailed networks to a skeletal or summary network for reporting purposes.

Network Integration—The joining of networks by interfacing to produce a master network reflecting the total program.

Optimistic Time Estimate (a)—The time in which the activity can be completed if everything goes exceptionally well. It is estimated that an activity would have no more than one chance in a hundred of being completed within this time.

PERT—A set of principles, methods, and techniques which enables the institution and continuance of effective planning, scheduling, costing, control, and cycling in the management of objective-oriented work by the use of:

- Graphic network based on a Work Breakdown Structure, which correctly sequences and relates interdependent activities and events in the work program at necessary level of detail
- Elapsed-time estimates and measurement of critical time values along the paths in the network
- Analysis of the interrelated network and slack values as a basis for continuous evaluation of present and projected program status and the performance of necessary corrective management action to secure timely accomplishment of program objectives.

Pessimistic Time Estimate (b)—An estimate of the longest time an activity would require under the most adverse conditions, barring acts of God.

Predecessor Event—See *Beginning Event*.

Program Breakdown Structure—See *Work Breakdown Structure*.

Program Management Network—A network reflecting the total program acquisition plan containing a level of detail required by the program manager for overall planning and control of the entire program.

Program Manager—The person assigned the prime responsibility for overall management of a program such as a program director (SPD) of a SPO or a project officer.

Scheduled Completion Date (T_S)—A date assigned for completion of an activity (or occurrence of an event) for purposes of planning and control *within* an organization.

Scheduled Elapsed Time (t_s)—The period of time assigned for performing an activity from which earliest and latest completion dates (S_E, S_L) are calculated.

Scheduling—Determination and assignment of scheduled time to events and activities as compared to "expected time" resulting from network computations.

Short Path Flag—A flag assigned to all activities leading to a common end event. The minimum time through these activities instead of the maximum time will be taken as the end event's expected date.

Shred-out—The extraction of selected items of pertinent data from the basic computed data for reporting to specific functions, areas, or levels of management interest.

Slack—For an *event*, slack is the difference between the latest allowable date and the expected date $(T_L - T_E)$ expressed in weeks. It is the same as the least algebraic value of slack for all activities ending with that event.

For an *activity*, slack is the difference between the latest allowable date of the ending event (T_L) and the expected completion date of the activity. When using PERT/COST, this is expressed as $S_L - S_E$.

Standard Deviation of an Activity (σ)—A measure of variance about the expected elapsed time for an activity, calculated when using three-time estimates. It is computed from the formula $b - a/6$.

Standard Deviation of an Event—A measure of variance about the event expected date. It is calculated by computing the square root of the sum of the squares of activity standard deviation on the longest time path leading to the event under consideration.

Successor Event—See *Ending Event.*

Summary Network—See *Program Management Network.*

Variance of an Activity (σ^2)—The square of the activity standard deviation.

Variance of an Event—The sum of the activity variance along the most time-consuming path leading to the referenced event.

Work Package—The unit of work required to complete a specific job or process, such as a report, a design, a document, a piece of hardware, or a service. The content of a Work Package may require the contributing services of several operating units, although the overall responsibility for the Work Package should be assigned to a single organization or responsible individual.

Work (Program) Breakdown Structure—A family-tree subdivision of a program, beginning with the end objectives and then subdividing these objectives into successively smaller End Item Subdivisions. The Work Breakdown Structure establishes the framework for:

• Defining the work to be accomplished
• Constructing a network plan
• Summarizing the cost and schedule status of a program for progressively higher levels of management

Zero-Time Activity—An activity which constrains the beginning of a following activity or occurrence of the event to which it leads by requiring that the event from which it proceeds occurs first.

Index

223